WOODLAND PLANTS

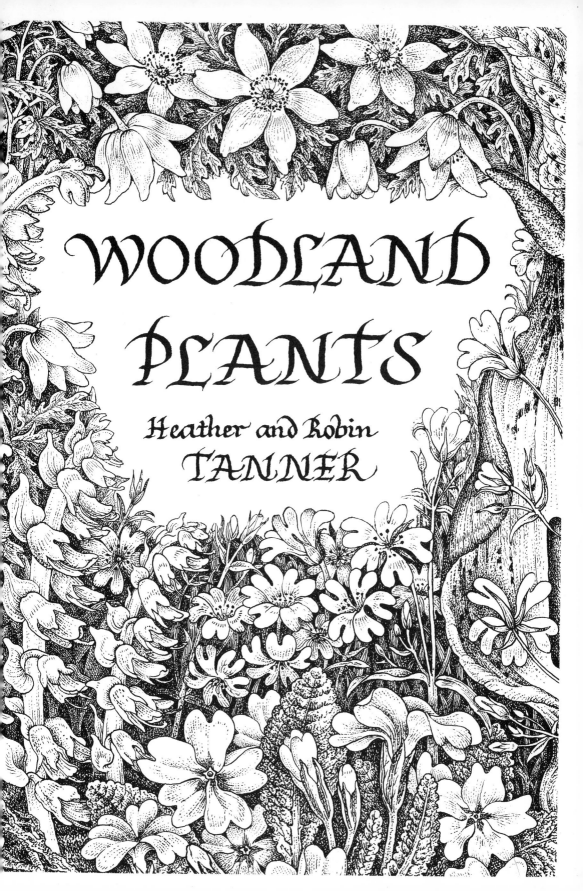

WOODLAND PLANTS

Heather and Robin TANNER

WOODLAND PLANTS

by
HEATHER TANNER
with illustrations by
ROBIN TANNER

IMPACT BOOKS

First published in 1981 by Robin Garton Ltd

Published in this paperback edition in 1987
by Impact Books, 112 Bolingbroke Grove,
London SW11 1DA

British Library Cataloguing in Publication Data
Tanner, Heather
    Woodland plants.
    1. Forest flora – Great Britain
    I. Title   II. Tanner, Robin
    582.13'9041   QK306

    ISBN 0-245-54606-5

Printed and bound in Great Britain
by R J Acford Ltd, Chichester, Sussex

I pull a flower from the woods —
A monster with a glass
Computes the stamens in a breath
And has her in a class.
Emily Dickinson.

How often have I stood by something of an uncommon beauty and absorbing it into my bones, yet failed to translate it into a mental image by which, escaping commonplace, I could carry the essence away with me, unfading.

H. J. Massingham: Shepherd's Country ch. 1.

Foreword

This is not a botany book, though it is indebted to many. It is a labour of love—love of the countryside and especially of its wild flowers—gradually taking shape during the last forty years. Our original ambition was to record every wild plant, in drawings and in writing, as it appeared. Needless to say, in a busy life, often thwarted by bad weather, this soon proved impossible, especially in spring. Moreover we soon found that the more we discovered the more we needed to know, and year after year would pass from buds to withered 'kexes' with nothing achieved. It became clear that we should have to limit ourselves. So many of the plants that most appealed to us were of the woodland that this suggested the first restriction—though again, which preferred woodland and which hedge? We should have to be arbitrary anyway, for there are hundreds that never leave the woods. Of these there were many that we had never seen growing, nor were likely to without expert help and much travelling. Meanwhile life was getting shorter—'had we so many springs allotted us?' We would limit ourselves to the plants we actually knew and which most asked to be drawn, while I would reluctantly abandon still further research and draw on the limited material I already had.

The book thus represents very much a personal choice, not aggressively but of necessity, to be liked or otherwise on that score. We ourselves regret omissions and inadvertent errors more than anybody. It could never have been completed without the ready help of others—the many friends who showed us their secret 'sites', the many more who took an interest in the work and continually encouraged us, and especially my sister, who not only criticised, helped research and typed, but provided a refuge where I could write without interruption.

Heather Tanner.

Hazel

The Drawings in 'Woodland Plants'

I started to make a record of woodland plants in January 1940, drawing winter aconite and stinking hellebore late that month in the snow. Because I wanted to show each plant growing in its setting I also drew dead leaves and twigs and beech mast, moss and lichen and snail shells, and whatever captured my attention on the woodland floor; and I made studies of various woodscapes that I knew well and wanted to introduce into the final drawings. I decided that each plant must be drawn its natural size: to make a bluebell larger or smaller than it is would be to create a quite different flower. This decision raised the problem of portraying each plant adequately in a rectangle whose maximum size I envisaged as 7" by 5". Foxglove, monkshood and many others, I realised, would call for careful arrangement to make this possible. I also determined from the start to pick no flower or leaf from any but the commonest plants: I must draw them *in situ*, uncomfortably kneeling if necessary, and maybe using a lens to see the complicated construction of some of the smaller ones.

So throughout 1940 I filled a book with several hundred detailed pencil drawings of plants as they bloomed. Yet at that high moment of late spring when so many plants flowered at once I was of course defeated, and in each succeeding year I tried to fill in the gaps in my record, often missing the perfect moment for lack of time. Ultimately there were almost a thousand drawings.

My resolve to see and draw each plant actually growing rather than as a cut specimen often meant long delays, and in one case—oxlip—I was driven to raising my own flowers from seed of a wild plant that was made available to me. After I had made many drawings of a particular flower it became clear that there were distinct variations in size and shape from plant to plant. Celandine, primrose, anemone and water avens, for example, exhibit this conspicuouly, and it was necessary sometimes to arrive at a mean, an average, to portray what might be called a typical plant.

I made each final pen drawing by surrounding myself with my studies, referring to them as I composed the plate and—in a world of black and white

11

only—trying to compensate for the absence of colour by emphasising the variety of textures and tones and the characteristic forms of stalks and leaves and flowers and fruits. The fruits and seedheads of many of the plants I studied seemed to me as beautiful and arresting as the flowers themselves, so aconite and hellebore and Spiked Star of Bethlehem were doubly celebrated.

Robin Tanner.

Contents

The Wood through the Year

It is February, but the winter has been hard, and spring is late. There is more evidence of last year than of this. The hedges are untidy with tousled withered grass and strangling clematis; even a few lustreless seedy blackberries linger. The birds have left hips here and there, and privet berries abound. In the keen wind the dead leaves and stalks rustle like paper, and it might well be incredible that the frost-parched earth had ever produced, or ever would produce, young life. How long ago the fields of summer seem! and yet the one thing certain is that they will flower again, abundant as ever—there is proof in the rosettes of thistle and ragwort where once the high meadow was purple and gold.

It should be more sheltered within the wood, which usually yields a primrose or two even in December. There have been flowers, for beside the wet path are forget-me-not stems; there in the ditch are traces of figwort, and here in the clearing bugle leaves. Ivy, hartstongue and male fern grow everywhere, disguising the bareness of the earth. No, not bareness—unfruitfulness; for bare it is not; there is hardly an inch uncovered. Mostly it is broken wood and leaves, but what wood, and what leaves! Some of the bark has been gnawed into raw patches by hungry animals in the hard frost. On this hazel bough, when it was wet, fell a sycamore leaf, and there it stayed until it became stencilled on part of the fabric. Some twigs are sprinkled with brilliant 'coral spot', or fringed with a soft, mossy growth of bluish greenish grey lichen, or covered with dark fungus. There are skeleton leaves of holly, curled crisp beech leaves, and oak leaves spotted with tiny grey eggs, lying among empty acorn cups, pillaged hazelnuts, pine cones and pine needles, woodpigeons' feathers, moss, close as plush or loose and starry, and snail shells. So many snail shells, and so many kinds! of all sizes from the large brown common snail to Lilliputians so tiny that it is hard to pick them up. Most conspicuous are the big bleached shells, palest grey marked with lilac, housing within their empty hollows smaller shells, some ribbed and whelk-shaped, some like miniature Roman shells, others flatter

B

17

and handsomely curled on the underside like a horn. The gayest are the 'cricket caps', yellow with brown spirals, brown with yellow spirals, blue and violet, or rosy pink all over. Now is the time of year to see these things: later they will be hidden under a carpet of flowers. Now too the rays of the sun still strike almost horizontally, showing colours far more brightly than in the height of summer—vivid moss on tree-trunks, the white lenticels on hazel twigs, the bare spray of wild briar, acid green below, plum purple above, with brown thorns and crimson buds.

Hazel catkins should have been ripe weeks ago; as it is they are full length on one bush only, always the same bush, in the lee of the wood. There is nothing so satisfying—welcoming one might call it—as finding a special plant in its special place year after year; nothing so disappointing as to come one day and see it is no longer there; nothing so exasperating as to forget the exact spot where it should be and hunt for it in vain.

Below are the early leaves of dog's mercury, the surest sign of approaching spring on the woodland floor as are the catkins on the hazels, the honeysuckle's double tongues of green flame in the undergrowth, and fresh cow parsley foliage in the hedges. And in the evening, subdued but unmistakable, are heard the first wild flutings of the missel thrush, mingling with the piping treble of the robin, that has sung all the winter.

A fortnight passes. The pussy willow is changing from silver to gold, while on the female bushes grey-green 'cones' appear. By the water, beneath the alders rich with crimson catkins and purple buds, are two marsh marigolds in full bloom. At a distance the wood may look wintry as ever, but against the dark hollies the sycamore buds show light green and fat, almost ready to break, and on one beech tree 'deep in the middle of the wood', where the floor is thickly strewn with tiny green moschatel, 'the folded leaf is wooed from out the bud'. Now there is young wild arum thrusting its way through all obstacles and crowned with the dead leaves it has speared. The growing nettles may sting before they are seen, for they are olive brown, the same colour as the surrounding earth. So it is that the dark young anemones are passed unnoticed until they are in bud; then see one and the wood is suddenly full of them, still curled up as they are coaxed through the earth.

The air is still so biting that one would expect little progress as the weeks go on. No-one could wish the cuckoo to come back to these inhospitable

The Woodland in Winter

winds and snow. Yet though cold does certainly make a difference in the supply of the special kind of foods they seek, birds seem less afraid of inclement weather than are human beings. Here is March the twenty-first, unpropitious as the first day of spring often is, and here sure enough is the chiffchaff, still a little hesitant, back at his wonted spot. White violets are only a little later than usual, young leaves of sanicle and pignut cover the ground, anemones are showing white—everything is just a stage further on.

At last comes a short spell of warm weather touching the earth like magic. No more, alas, are there tall elms red against the blue sky, but larch and willow are in flower, elder and chestnut in leaf, and incessant 'chiff-chaffs' almost drown the 'weep, weep' of the newly arrived willow warbler. In the wood, now littered with primroses, the whole of the coming year can be foretold. Clusters of bluebell spikes, the trefoils of wood sorrel—these one would expect by now; but though the hot dusty holiday time of 'farewell summer' meadowsweet is yet far off here are its leaves, 'just to the time'. One is filled with wonder—and with shame; wonder that this miracle is repeated spring after spring, and shame that man now seems set for a world where no trees burgeon and no swallow returns.

This is the time to play a game of guessing which plants are which. This will be golden archangel and this red campion: how lovely May will be! Here are two closely wrapped leaves; soon the centre will shoot up into a twayblade flower. What looks like garden goldenrod is gromwell; that woolly cabbage is a young mullein, and that is not dew shining in the sun, but the silver hairs of young hogweed leaves. A prickly, blistered rosette spread on the ground close by is easily identified by last year's dried teazle brushes. A small pink-tipped plant, with a pattern of yellowish leaves that look as though they had grown in partial darkness, is at first a puzzle; then it takes on a more familiar look. Of course it is rosebay willow-herb, rose now not in flower but in leaf. Why, the warm protective colour is everywhere!— Alice Meynell's 'colour of Life', H. J. Massingham's 'madder, the colour of Spring'. The small perforated leaves of St. John's Wort too are backed with pink, a strawberry pink in harmony with the blue-grey of the upper surface. Seen at close quarters, the fallen hazel catkin's pollen is not brown but deep orange; the sycamore bud's discarded scales are flushed. Stem and midrib of greater willow-herb, now half a foot high, run carmine. And here the wood seems full of flowers like little red larch cones. They are the tips of the wood

The Woodland floor in Winter

spurge plants, which bend over and show the undersides of their leaves, dyed as brilliantly as the stems. More subtle but not less lovely are the bronze and copper hues—in the veins and centres of celandine leaves, in leaves of aconite, anemone, bugle, ground ivy, elder.

The unwonted warmth has wooed out the brimstone butterflies, here one, there a pair, there another, and more and more of them, as though the brightest of the primroses had taken wing. Blue-black beetles too feel spring in their 'veins': they are everywhere in couples, the smaller male specially shod with orange grips that will hold firmly to the orange back of his mate. A grass snake wriggles into the undergrowth.

But no matter how thick the stars in wood and hedgerow, spring is not truly here till the cuckoo comes. Then, once launched, there is no keeping up with the season; it rushes pell-mell into May. By now the nightingale too has arrived; if to hear him before the cuckoo's first note portends success in love, as Milton says, then the course of true love never did run smooth. Scarcely has his last liquid note died away when 'the innumerable choir of day welcome the dawn'. Now and at evening thrush and blackbird are most clamorous, but with calling and bubbling cuckoo, great tit and chiffchaff, whitethroat and dunnock, wren and willow wren, chaffinch and greenfinch, blackcap and garden warbler, they also sing tirelessly all day. The turtledove returns to her old haunt in the thicket, the woodpigeon (or the more recently arrived collared dove) claps his wings as he flies over the tops of the greening beeches. The wild cherry is 'hung with bloom along the bough'; oaks become golden; only a few ashes and walnuts still hesitate.

Now is the very time when everything grows together or in rapid succession, for May is supremely the month of woodland flowers. What is that mysterious understanding as to spheres of influence that appears to be arrived at, and accommodation for all secured? Roots reaching to different levels are part of the secret, arbitrary changes or disturbances in the pattern of local soil and climate another. First bluebells 'stand about the woodland ride' into the misty distance, while nearer the air is full of their strong sweet smell; then garlic, wood spurge, woodruff, wood sanicle, goldilocks, archangel, wood forget-me-not, bugle, wild strawberry and the rarer lilies and orchids—lily-of-the-valley, Solomon's seal, butterfly and bird's-nest orchid and the helleborines. Short as is the blossoming time of each kind of flower, almost equally amazing is the way those same flowers linger here

The Woodland floor in early Spring

and there. Celandine and dog's mercury may be still out, though most of their plants are in fruit and showing large handsome leaves, and there are still primroses and violets, a little untidy on their long stems.

May overruns its confines as well as its seasons. Where hedgerows have escaped today's slaughter there are still 'little rows of sportive wood run wild', with dripping fountains of hairy brome grass, and bluebells, foxgloves, ground ivy and honeysuckle covering the banks, while some wood-lovers like daffodils, horsetail and betony also invade the meadows. Typical woodland plants however have a character of their own. Many are specially fitted to withstand the rigours of early spring: those with bulbs or underground stems draw on them for food; spurge laurel and butcher's broom brave the snow with evergreen leaves and need grow no new ones in spring; garlic and snowdrop hood their flowerbuds with sheaths; the daffodil resists the gale with swiftly turned narrow blades; anemone leaves look fragile, but they are deeply cut and the wind blows harmlessly through them; wood sorrel and celandine close their flowers in inclement weather. Woodland plants cope too with shortage of light. The butterfly orchid has a sweet scent as if to lure into the depths of the dark wood insects that might not otherwise suspect its presence. Nor is it surprising to find many greenflowered plants, that press petals as well as leaves into the service of turning light into energy—spurge laurel and wood spurge, green and stinking hellebore, dog's mercury, twayblade and moschatel, all but the last three of these being poisonous as an additional insurance for survival. Moreover, although the woods hold no monopoly of rare plants, it is in their depths more than anywhere that they are to be found. Woods hold the secrets, known only to a few, of the whereabouts of asarabacca, columbine, red helleborine, the almost extinct martagon lily, and lady's slipper orchid, now reduced to a single plant. Has their very rarity made them conspicuous, or is it due to their lack of the usual woodland defences?

All this contrivance for survival in a limited and shared environment is familiar today as 'ecology', and our adult pleasures in the pathless woods are enhanced by recognition of the science/art/philosophy from which we have so much to learn. Our childhood was irresponsibly free of it. 'The stars were mine, and so were the sun and moon, and all the world was mine, and I the only spectator and enjoyer of it,' says Traherne of his childhood. In the same sense the woods were mine, the burnished gold of celandines mine to hoard,

24

The Woodland in Spring

the scent of primroses among moss mine to bury the face in, the bluebells with the most bells mine, I am afraid, mine to pick—for although we were always adjured to pluck carefully, never more than we needed, and never never to throw down, picking was not then regarded as robbery of future generations. With no idea that fields and woods were owned and controlled, we were outraged if turned out of what we considered our wood of fairytale and romance by a gamekeeper, who since he carried a gun must be cruel— our child minds not unnaturally construing the 'prosecution' of trespassers as persecution if not execution.

We were filled with dismay too when 'our' hazels were slaughtered, not knowing that this could be good woodcraft and that they would grow again, and better, from the stools, while the following year a carpet of primroses, rejoicing in the new light and space, might be discerned there from afar as never before. We were disconcerted when 'our' patch of some cherished plant was missing from its special place. Some didactic 'Uncle George' should have shown us the creeping underground stems by which it had reached what it considered a more favourable position. Of pinewoods we were afraid: they were impenetrable, flowerless and gloomy. Today we might fear them more as an alien invasion for purely monetary gain. The sixteenth century discovered the danger of destroying without replanting woodland, though not before Scotland had become virtually treeless; and now the spread of deserts throughout the world, the threat of alteration to climate, the creation of dustbowls, and in our own country the recent ravages of Dutch elm disease, have started us thinking, it may not be too late. To preserve the quality of life, thirty per cent of this land, we now learn, should be woodland.

In the July wood a new colour spreads among the trees. First there was the gold of aconite and celandine, then the white of anemone, wood sorrel, garlic, then bluebells. Now it is a crude gaudy magenta, stretches and stretches of it where rosebay willow-herb covers the clearings between the pines, columns of it where foxgloves tower among the pungent bracken. Enchanter's nightshade too is everywhere, the inconspicuous little flowers looking more like seeds. Indeed in August the aptness of the metaphor 'seedy' is very apparent. Superficially the wood is dull and dishevelled. There is little birdsong, and for all the varying shades of spring green there are now only two—deciduous and evergreen. The foxglove bells climb

26

The Woodland floor in Autumn

further and further up the stalk, leaving their fruits below, and the forget-me-not's only beauty now is the regular pattern of its seeds laddering the stem. The rosebay flame dies to puffs of smoke, floating here, there and everywhere. Bracken begins to turn brown and wither.

So do the leaves, first those of the yellowing ash that was first to show colour. The chestnut's gold, redder than the pale coin-gold of the mourned elms, is soon stripped. The oaks are russet as when they were tasselled with catkins, but now it is not black pollen grains but leaves that patter down. The elder hangs its heavy wet berries from bare branches.

But if all things else seem dying, the fungi are very much alive: huge white oystershells making platforms high up in the dead tree-trunks; verdigris agaric, the colour of a thrush's egg, under the pines; amethyst agaric, that looks so suspect but is good to eat; scarlet, white-spotted fly agaric beside the path; the embarrassing stinkhorn, Phallus impudicus, risen fly-infested from its broken ball; and everywhere among the dead leaves and on fallen logs, singly and in colonies, toadstools of every shade of yellow, cream and brown, shaped like parasols, like horns, like arum lilies, like pancakes, like buttons, like buns, like hats, like sponges, like tables.

When these have all degenerated into a dark, slimy similarity the wood settles down for the winter. Under the beeches the dried 'kexes' of bird's-nest orchid, stem and fruit hard and ribbed and brown, stand sentinel; they will still be there when the new plants come up. So even they, lifeless as though they had never lived, are an earnest of spring, like the hazels that among their withered leaves have already put forth tight catkins.

Winter Aconite buds in snow

WINTER ACONITE
Eranthis hyemalis

It is a sad truth that any plant that takes to civilised quarters in park or estate loses caste as a wild flower. Like Daphne mezereon, winter aconite is found more often in gardens than in woods; like many of our woodland plants it was not originally British, but a native of Southern Europe that has been naturalised. Nevertheless it is found, even though rarely, in copses and hedges far from human habitation where, even if it was once planted deliberately, it has grown wild for centuries.

It 'thrusteth up . . . out of the ground, in the deepe of winter oftentimes, if there be any milde weather in January, but most commonly after the deepe frosts, bearing up many times the snow upon the heads of the leaves' (Parkinson). The early stages of its unfolding may be easily missed, for there is so little sign of spring when it first appears that the world seems still frozen into the winter of the previous year, and no-one would dream yet of looking for new growth. Yet there it is, a small crooked olive-coloured staple driven into the olive-coloured earth. Snow falls, and the young aconite rises through and above it, revealing itself as a tight bud curled under the stem like the top of a shepherd's staff; the warmth engendered by its growth thaws a tiny pool in the snow round the stalk. Each bud unfolds into a single flower, or into a leaf that may keep the brown tinge of its babyhood, but is more often a rich green, in shape three, four or five-fold, and deeply cut into long thin fingers—a little like a leaf of monkshood perhaps. Gerard writes: 'If the scorpion passe by where it groweth and touch same, presently he becommeth dull, heavie and senceless', which suggests some narcotic influence, but it is not poisonous, and this fancied similarity of leaf and the family name Ranunculus are all that the true, the deadly aconite (monkshood) has in common with *Eranthis hyemalis,* the 'wintry spring' flower.

The flower buds uncurl, first turning sideways, when they look like little golden faces hidden in the depths of green-fringed poke bonnets which they turn against the wind for shelter. Gradually the bonnets are folded back, and now the upturned heads are wearing neck-ruffs; or you may see them as

Winter Aconite

yellow cups on green saucers. The saucer is actually a whorl of bracts, the cup sepals, six, seven or eight, while the true petals are little tubes full of nectar, ranged around the crowded stamens.

Where aconites flourish their very earliness makes them conspicuous. Under a hidden sun they shine all along the bank at the fringe of the wood, alone courageously insisting on living spring in a world of winter. Much the same size as the celandine, they are in bloom a month earlier, and far, far earlier than the buttercup which in flower and in leaf they more nearly resemble. Their gold is not as bright as the celandine's, not as rich as the buttercup's, not glossy as theirs is, but a duller, more transparent colour that at last begins to look cold and sodden as the edges turn inwards and the flower fades.

Seed-heads of Winter Aconite

STINKING HELLEBORE

Helleborus foetidus

In the depths of winter a copse can look very arid: it seems to need a good springclean. Bleached stems and stringy nettle-stalks lie strewn in all directions over a tangle of brambles that here and there imprison a pool of forgotten snow. But if the wood is on limestone or chalk we may be cheered by a very different pattern traced on the snow—the dark green serrated fan of hellebore leaves spreading like a palm, or as country people fancied, like the print of a many-toed bear's foot.

It is the commoner stinking hellebore, evergreen, with narrower leaves than the green hellebore's, that we have stumbled on. The name is inaccurate: it has an acrid, not foetid smell, unmistakably poisonous, and hardly distinguishing, since all hellebores have it more or less. All are handsome—our two wild ones, and in our gardens the Christmas Rose, the purple Lenten Rose, the Corsican, and the many hybrids.

Growing in a cluster, the stinking hellebore's drooping bells are of so pale a green against the blackish tone of their leaves as to seem at a distance, caught by the slanting winter sunlight, almost primrose yellow. The bells are edged with the same wine colour that suffuses the whole flower of the Lenten Rose. One must not call these petals, for technically they are sepals, the true petals, like the winter aconite's, having been modified into nectaries. This is a great advantage to both wild flower seeker and gardener, for the non-petals, unlike true petals that fall when their work of attracting fertilising insects is done, persist through the season and beyond, still looking like flowers as they hold the huge triple-peapod fruits, while the leaves grow ever larger and the whole gracefully branching plant ever taller.

The common name is setter-wort (from Latin *sutare,* to sew) because of its use as a charm sewn into the ear or dewlap of an animal. William Turner discovered this folklore when travelling in Germany in the middle of the sixteenth century, and returned to find it practised at home: 'A certayne wyse Germane, yet unlearned in the Latin tonge, when he perceived that I was desirous to know herbes and the natures of the same, asked me whether

C

33

I knewe an herbe called in theyr tonge Christwurtz or no. I sayde ye, but knowe you sayeth he, all the properties that it hathe. I shewed hym of certayne properties . . . well saythe he, I know more properties that it hathe besyde thys, and forthewyth tolde me that apece of the roote put into a beastes ere . . . heleth the beast of any inwarde desease. When I came into England I dyd hear that dyverse husband men used to put the roote of berefoot into beastes eares and called the puttinge in of it Syterynge of beastes and in sume place called the herbe syter wurte. They saye it shulde be used thus: the brodest parte of the ear must have a rounde circle made about it wyth the blood that ryneth furth, wyth a brasene botkyne[1], and the same circle must be rounde lyke unto the letter O, and in the hygher part of the eare the halfe of the foresayd cyrcle is to be bored thorowe wyth the foresayd botkyne, and the rote of the herbe is to be put in at the hole, whyche when the newe wounde hath receyved, holdeth it so faste that it will not let it goo forth; and then all the myght and pestilent poysen of the disease is brought so into the eare. And whylles the part whyche is circled aboute dyeth and falleth awaye, the hole beast is saved wyth the lose of a very smalle parte.'

Spenser in his *Shepherds' Calender* (July) alludes to the herb as a sheep salve, and Virgil's *Georgics,* Book III, gives the recipe:

> the shorn bodies are smeared with bitter olive-lees,
> And a salve is compounded of silver oxide, native sulphur,
> Pitch, emollient wax-paste,
> Squills and stinking hellebore and black bitumen.[2]

[1] Avoiding the black magic use of iron.
[2] Trans. C. Day Lewis [Cape 1946].

Stinking Hellebore in snow

Fruit of Stinking Hellebore

DOG'S MERCURY

Mercurialis perennis

Anyone who has experienced an exceptionally hard winter knows what it is to feel a primitive panic lest the universe should have gone rogue and the world ceased to turn. Though it is late March the whole stricken landscape is inky black and grey, littered where no brief gleam of sun has penetrated with patches of snow. Then one day, in the bank on the sheltered side of the wood, incredibly there is a different patch—of fresh green, a chorus of the V signs of dog's mercury leaves thrusting up from the long-lifeless earth, bringing sudden hope like that of rainbow after Deluge. Spring will come: spring is here; and day by day the living green is eagerly watched till the leaves unfold and the flowers appear, like fountains of little yellow-green beads strung on a thread.

These are the male flowers, but their resemblance to seeds led to confusion even among botanists. The female flowers are borne later, on a less common plant, to become two round ovaries like goosegrass balls. The female variety also grows in colonies, adjacent to though separate from the male; but the plant scarcely needs fertilisation, since it spreads by its rootstock far and rapidly, a woodland carpet ever darker and bluer green as spring turns to summer.

It was the god Mercury who is said to have revealed the medicinal properties of the plant—not however of this perennial kind but of the annual mercury, sometimes found as a weed in or near gardens. 'Dog's', as in dog-rose, dog-violet, is a warning of inferiority of quality, but the curative powers of both kinds vary dangerously according to the herbalist. Culpeper for instance says, 'it is wonderful (if not fabulous) what Dioscorides and Theophrastus relate of it, viz. That if women use these herbs either inwardly or outwardly for three days after conception, they shall bring forth male or female children according to that kind of herb they use', which sounds like the 'doctrine of signatures'—the old belief that the outward form of a plant was the clue to its medicinal use—deduced from the male and female plants of dog's mercury. It is a relief to know that neither perennial nor annual is now used internally!

C*

For the ordinary person it cannot have been very essential to distinguish these: it was more important to know dog's mercury from orache ('Good King Henry' or 'Fat Hen'), with which, before the introduction of our cultivated variety, the poor man's spinach, it was occasionally and disastrously confused, superficial though the resemblance is. Anne Pratt's cook once gave her dog's mercury leaves in mistake for mint, and here the resemblance is even less, scent apart: for dog's mercury leaves are much larger, with beautifully intricate veining. This convinced Anne of the error of the superstition that poison can be destroyed by cooking, and may have given her her ghoulish obsession with poisonous plants.

Dog's Mercury (male and female)

SNOWDROP

Galanthus nivalis

Is there a creature so calloused that he has no special feeling for the snow-drop? Herein there is great hope for man, whatever his general depravity. The snowdrop has no colour, exhales a perfume so faint that it is usually detectable only by the early bees for which it is intended; it yields no salves or simples. It is loved partly for its bravery in thrusting through the wintry soil, partly for its promise of the spring nowhere else apparent, but chiefly for its purity and innocence, and whoso is aware of that has in him poetry.

The first sign of it, early in January, is a stubbly growth of grey-green leaf tips, and among them little flower buds like pointed bulbs wrapped in silvery sheaths, and tipped with a rib of green. Well might the French call them 'perce-neige': they pierce not only the snow but everything that comes in their way; they make a bee-line upwards through pine-needles and moss and withered leaves, which as they grow they carry in triumph as trophies on the points of their lances. Gradually each firm white bud, still upstanding, works free of its protective sheath, then turns sideways like a daffodil and droops from the polished emerald-green knob that joins it to the stem. The sheath disappears, and only the double bract stands up like a little horn above the bent bud. This is its loveliest, its 'snowdrop' phase—the word is so inevitable that it has eclipsed all other names save 'February Fairmaid'. The two leaves grow longer and curve more freely on either side. And now it is a 'Schneeglöckchen', a snow bell; the sepals, still keeping their protective curve, part like panniers over a dress to reveal the green-bordered heart-shaped petals. Within they store nectar—and to good purpose, for at the end of May the hard green fruits prove that every bloom, however unpropitious the weather, has been fertilised. Too soon the flowers are fully out, their first beauty already lost, and galaxies of them show dazzling white against the dark evergreens. *Galanthus nivalis* does indeed emphasise their whiteness, calling them first 'milk flower', then 'snowy'.

Gerard did not number snowdrops among wild flowers: 'These plants doe growe wilde in Italie and the places adjacent: notwithstanding our

Snowdrop

London gardens have taken possession of them manie yeares past', and Sowerby, unable to find a wild snowdrop, drew a garden specimen. Even so they have found our soil so much to their liking that whole woods, mainly in the north of England, may be thickly covered with them. The North: everything about them breathes frigidity—all around, blue shadows on the snow; above, the blue of the holly leaves whose polished surfaces reflect the frosty sky; the bloom on their own narrow blades that are cold to the touch; their perfect icy whiteness.

Snowdrop buds

SPURGE LAUREL

Daphne laureola

It is at the bleakest moment of winter that the spurge laurel comes into its own, oasis in the desert—in more ways than one, for its tall strong woody stems, ridged and bare, each surmounted by its crown of fresh evergreen leaves, suggest a miniature plantation of date palms. It is rather like a spurge, though nothing like the laurel into which Daphne was transformed to escape the pursuit of Apollo, but since evergreen it is 'laurel' in common parlance.

No flowers will be seen till March, crowding beneath their whorl of leaves, and they may continue in bloom well into April if the bees have not had enough warmth and sun to collect the plentiful nectar stored in their pendent clusters of waxy green bells. Virgil says that the plant should be put near hives.

In Britain it is found only in England, mainly southern England, and on limestone. The related Daphne mezereon is much rarer: indeed being now almost confined to Cornwall it can hardly be called wild, having perhaps been too sought after for the exquisite scent and delicate pink colour of its flowers. Gardeners have tried to crossbreed the two Daphnes without success, though Daphne mezereon has been grafted onto the woodland plant.

Spurge laurel berries turn first red, then black. In Cockayne's Leechdoms the seeds are called Githcorn: 'Against hardness of the innards take the seed of this wort, that are, the grains, well cleaned; take to drink in warm water. Soon it stirs the innards.' Being poisonous, it certainly would. On the other hand the acrid bark of either Daphne, of either root or stem, has been used to raise blisters and for poultices, and is admitted to the British pharmacopoeia.

Spurge Laurel

GREEN HELLEBORE
Helleborus viridis

Green hellebore is much rarer than the stinking, though that may be partly because of its use in medicine in the past, for it was our nearest approach to the classical 'black' hellebore ('black' being used by the old herbalists for the variety described by the earliest authorities), which was probably the Christmas Rose. It is herbaceous, not evergreen, is found only on calcareous soil, and not before March (whereas the stinking hellebore blooms earlier), and is very local, though where it does grow it is easy to see in its small colony of fanned-out leaves, perhaps between wood and roadside, and apparently in flower for weeks on end. Moreover it is the largest green flower in Britain, two inches across when fully open. The colour however is less conspicuous than the stinking hellebore's, leaves and sepals being the same clear apple green with a bluish bloom.

This flower is not bell-shaped but lies open like a green Christmas Rose, five outer sepals and an inner 'ring of drinking horns'[1]—the nectaries—encircling an especially beautifully designed centre of pale cream-coloured stamens, the nearest circle curving inwards and the riper spreading outwards all round. Little more than nine inches high when it first flowers, the green hellebore, like the stinking, will become taller and yet more stately with the progress of spring.

Why, since it was supposed by one herbalist to be the plant 'with which the unjust Athenians made to die wise Socrates', was it so prized in medicine? In 1400 B.C. one Melampus used it to cure madness, giving it 'Melampone' as one of its many names. 'Ellebore' comes from two Greek roots, 'to expel' and 'food'. Emetic and purge it certainly was, and sneeze-inducer: one German name was Nieswurz. It expelled worms in children 'exceedingly', and sometimes fatally.

William Turner seems to consider green hellebore a wild plant and stinking hellebore a garden plant in England: 'I have seen bothe the kyndes in Englande: the one kynde in gardynes whych is wylde in Germany, and the

[1] E. J. Salisbury: *Flowers of the Woods.*

45

other kynde with the broder leaffe, whyche is onely in gardynes in Germany (as farre as I coulde perceyve), in Northumberlande in the weste parke besyde Morpeth a good stone cast from the water syde in the syde of the hylle.' He warns, 'The wylde kynde kylleth lyesse [lice], and not only lyesse but also shepe and other beastes if they do eate it: wherefore men had nede to take hede how that they take it.'

One can only hope there was some truth in the theory of the Grete Herball of 1526:[1] 'In olde tyme it was commely used in medycyns . . . For the body of man was stronger that it is now, and myght better endure the vyolence of elebore, for man is weyker at this time of nature.'

[1] Translated from the French and printed by Peter Treveris.

Green Hellebore

LESSER CELANDINE

Ranunculus ficaria

March may be a succession of grey weeks of 'blight' as country people call it—bleak sunless days that seem to suspend the sap in the branch and the blood in the veins. Then unannounced comes a day 'to show how costly summer is at hand.' The air is soft, the skies are clear, countless yellow stars that seem to have caught all the warmth of the young sun in their brilliance shine in every hazel copse and hedge bank. These celandines must have been long in flower, for there are faded silver stars among the gold, but they count only the sunny hours of midday and, folded close late and early and in cloudy weather, were passed unseen.

They are in every way lavish, not only in prolific growth but in variety. Even botanically there are two kinds, the rarer, which is shade-loving, setting no seed but reproducing vegetatively. They are quite indiscriminate in the number of their stamens (from twenty to sixty), and of their petals, normally eight, but often ten, or six set in a triangle. Some celandines are double, with inner rings of smaller petals turning in or out like those of a rose. John Rea (Flora 1665) found a double form in a field and distributed it throughout the country. Celandines play games with their leaves too, now varying their heart shapes lengthwise or widthwise, now edging them with scallops concave or convex, or spilling bronze through their veins or mottling them like cyclamen. The rosettes spread out close to the ground, basking in the sun, for at the end of spring they die away and yield up their strength to the roots.

It is these roots that have given the plant its name of *ficaria* or fig-like: the clustered tubers are not unlike a bunch of small brown figs. To the old herbalists they suggested haemorrhoids, so the conclusion was that 'pile-wort' as they called it was the cure for that complaint. According to Culpeper 'they say it helps the Hemorrhoids or Piles by only carrying it about one,' though he adds in a naïve parenthesis 'but if that it will not, bruise it and apply it to the grief.' It had other uses: 'Ye rootes being juiced are good with hony to be put into the nostrills for the purging of the head, as likewise the decoction thereof with Hony, being gargarised, doth powerfully purge the head, and all things out of the thorax' runs the Elizabethan version of Dioscorides, and Gilbert White says, 'The good women give the leaves powdered to children troubled with worms; but it is a violent remedy, and ought to be administered with caution.' It even had magic properties—if picked in the morning of St. Peter's day (June 29th) it would protect one from imprisonment!

Lesser Celandine

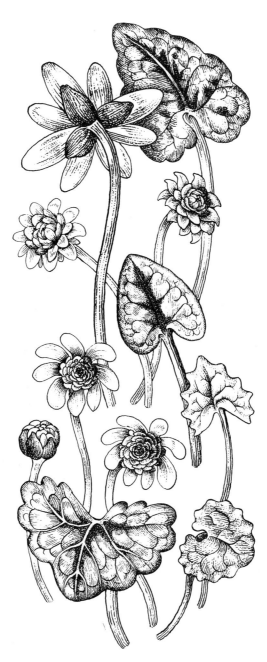

Lesser Celandine—variations in flowers and leaves

DAFFODIL

Narcissus pseudo-narcissus

Could there be a more devastating example of scientific fact totally divorced from imagination than such an insulting name for one of the world's most beautiful flowers?

The daffodil must be the best known of all our native wild flowers, but alas, not as a wild flower. Gardens have taken it over, and now there are not only double 'daffs' but all-yellows, all-whites, white-and-yellows, peach-coloureds, the trumpetless, and giants so heavy that a shower is enough to flatten them or break them to an ugly angle. Parkinson, the gardeners' botanist, devotes over forty pages to the varieties. Judiciously mingled and disposed they are delightful, but they are not wild daffodils, unsophisticated enough not to go 'blind' and need dividing; small enough to survive equinoctial gales and even snow, bending their brave little half-opened throats all one way; pedigree enough to keep the essential tone contrast—pale yellow perianth round a golden corona, the 'yellow petticoat and green gown' of the nursery rhyme. Few there must be who have seen them as the Wordsworths saw them in their nodding thousands, in still leafless woodland where they were 'never reaped and never sown'; and where they have taken to the fields the farmer may exploit them—pay your entrance fee and pick your fill.

'Daffodil' is a corruption of 'asphodel', though it is not the asphodel that with amaranth bloomed in the eternal spring of the Elysian fields. For the so-called 'unexplained D' we need surely look no further than the compulsion to reduplication and alliteration, as old and as universal as language itself. Indeed, why not yet another d—'daffadowndilly'? which brings the literary echoes crowding in: Spenser's

> Strowe me the ground with Daffadowndillies,
> And cowslips and kingcups and loved Lilies,

51

Milton's

> Bid amaranthus all his beauty shed
> And daffadillies fill their cups with tears
> To strew the laureat herse where Lycid lies,

and Jean Ingelow's poem with its alternating refrains of 'Persephone! Persephone!' and 'The daffodil! the daffodil!'

But Shakespeare has said it all:

> Daffodils
> That come before the swallow dares, and take
> The winds of March with beauty.

Daffodil

PRIMROSE
Primula vulgaris

In almost every month, here or there, and from March to May everywhere—far longer than the usual blossoming time—may be seen the slender tapering buds of the primrose and the fair, fresh, pink-stemmed flowers. There is nothing more moving, not even the sight of the first snowdrop, than to find on an arid winter's day an early primrose, miniature but fully out, with its innocence giving the lie to the surliness of the season. And even before the flowers bloom there are the leaves, themselves miracles of texture and design, thickly quilted all over in a maze of lines; woolly at the back, with the lines standing almost clear of the blade; crinkly edged, furled and narrow in youth, broadening and flattening as they grow.

The primrose is the year's 'firstling', and is called 'primerole' from 'primula' in the mediaeval books of medicine that reveal its wonderful properties; though popular speech, recognising no morphology but only the apt and the pretty, soon converted the name to 'primrose', which appears as a surname as early as the thirteenth century. 'For man or woman that losethe his speche for seknes' runs one mediaeval recipe (Henslow), 'take . . . the lef of primerole, and do it in his mouth, and he schale speke'. And another: 'For schakyng of hede and of handes. Take primerole with alle the rotes, lange [lungwort] with all the rotes, mustard seed and lorer leves, and of all the herbes liche miche [alike much—equal quantities], and let hem ben well grounden in a morter and wel medlit with may buttyre or other freshe buttyr that nevere com in water, and lat it stande so 4 dayes or 5, and after frye it in a panne, and clense it thurgh a cloth; and with that oynement anoynte the nekke and the synwes and the veynes and the Ioyntes of the handes.'

The 'oynement' has stood the test of time, for a salve is still made from the plant. Culpeper had great faith in it. 'Of the leaves of primroses is made as fine a salve to heal wounds as any I know;' he writes, 'do not see your poor neighbours go with wounded limbs when a halfpenny cost will heal them.' Gerard instances a London doctor who every May would dose his patients with a primrose cordial. Note May, and May butter—the fairies' month.

Primrose

It would be surprising if magic had not been found in so wellbeloved a flower. It has all the qualities men most love: a delicate pale luminous colour, more green than yellow, with a gold star in the centre; a shape so crisp and symmetrical that it might have been stamped out with a scalloped cutter; a fragrance fresher and more virginal than that of any other flower; and abundance of growth. For although it is the rarer flowers that are the more persecuted, they have not that place in the affections held by those that are spilled out with lavish generosity year after year.

For us children spring was not spring till we had gone 'primrosing'. We would search for the largest, giants two inches across, or for the pink ones, rare in the woods, though in Cornwall they seem as common as the yellow. The old belief that they will come up pink if planted upside down must have proved true often enough to persist. Of course we looked for the two kinds of flower, 'pin-eyed' and 'thrum-eyed', or 'girls and boys' as we called them, the first with the pistil and the second with the stamens uppermost—strange that this device for cross-pollinating should have been left to Darwin to discover.

Had we known it there were many more strange forms we might have found, which we still find today wild in our own field. The garden polyanthus has exploited the primrose form—many stems branching from a single one; in the wild their meeting place is mostly below ground, in the garden well above. All garden lovers now know, besides the double primrose, the 'hose-in-hose', one flower springing from the centre of another, and 'Jack-in-the-green', whose calyx becomes five little leaves which as they enlarge frame the growing flower with ever-varying patterns. Occasionally a similar trick is tried when the stamens change to pretty little petals round the central star, itself always at the game of finding new forms. Now we know what the botanists mean when they refer to spines as 'modified' leaves! There is infinite variety too in primrose petals apart from size, colour and number. Some are very deeply cut, others cut more than once—almost frilled; yet others are twisted like a child's paper windmill toy, or furled in slender quills.

In those days when we dared to pick we should have thought it impossible to exterminate the primrose. Easter after Easter (read Kilvert's Diary) were not church and churchyard filled with them, in bunches and mounds, wreaths and crosses? And where woodcutters had been with their carts did they not next year overflow the clearing as thickly as ever, bright against the darkness of the stacked faggots, taking root even in the crevices of the bark? But that was before the invention of the mechanised hedge-cutter that slashes its blind way a foot or two above ground, leaving the amputation to rot and choke the ditch where no living thing can grow, while between maimed hedges and the new barbed wire fence nettles and docks enjoy secure licence. Worse still is the hedge-grubber that dries the churned-up soil into the bargain. Nor is bad agriculture the only enemy: the growing keenness on gardening is not always innocent, and the countryman himself has been known to take a trowel to the woods for a quick effect on his road-facing bank. We may be pardoned for having thought of the primrose as typically English, part of our home and childhood. It grows still in most Continental countries. Shall we one day have to go there to see it in the wild?

A twin Primrose

Primrose, 'Jack-in-the-Green'

Variations of Primrose

MOSCHATEL

Adoxa moschatellina

Both these Latin names are irrelevant. The musk scent is undetectable unless at very close quarters in damp weather or at evening, although the persistence of 'musk' names in several languages shows, as in monkey musk and mignonette, that it was once stronger. *Adoxa* means 'without glory', but though no green-flowered plant four inches high could be called glorious this one can surely be described as unique.

A flower may be many-rayed like the sun, may hang like a bell, inward or outward turning, may make a star with four, five, six, seven, eight points, may resemble a gaping mouth or even a dangling puppet, but is there another shaped like a dice, or a town clock with four faces? Stranger still, while the four sides have each a five-fold flower—five sepals, five petals, ten stamens—the top square has a pattern of four—four sepals and petals, eight stamens. 'Fairy clocks' and 'Five-faced bishop' (although why bishop?) describe it well, and 'Good Friday flower' shows that it likes an early rather than a late Easter.

If in early April moschatel is inconspicuous, its whereabouts in the still leafless wood is quickly discovered by a scattering of green on the bare earth—the tiny plants coming up; for although Smith (Sowerby) says, 'We have never found the ripe fruit', they spread by seed, appearing in fresh places quite a distance away, as well as by the white burrowing rhizome commemorated in the queer name 'Small Bunnikens Holwoort' (hollow root). A little later the seedlings can easily be mistaken for miniature buttercup plants ('Musk crowfoot' is another name), but still later are more like fumitory—the original botanical description was *Moschatellina foliis Fumariae bulbosae*. Fullgrown, by which time the charming little yellow-green clocks are out, the leaf has taken on a shape that like the dice seems to have been deliberately designed, this time by an embroiderer: three leaflets to a stem, each divided into three lobes, each lobe again cut into three, silky above, shiny beneath. *Adoxa?* Not Solomon in all his glory was arrayed like one of these.

Moschatel

SWEET VIOLET
Viola odorata

Early in March the craving comes over one to find the first white violets.
Dog's mercury is growing in plenty, celandines are bright at midday, even a
premature primrose appears here and there, but these alone do not satisfy.
Violets there must be somewhere, for the children have searched them out.
At first they are deceived for every violet found:

> The shell of a little snail bleached
> In the grass; chip of flint, and mite
> Of chalk; and the small bird's dung
> In splashes of purest white:
> All the white things a man mistakes
> For earliest violets.[1]

Then, all at once it seems, there are so many that deceptions cease to be
disappointments.

Children know only white and blue, sweet and scentless, early and later
violets. Europe has seventy-five species, America sixty-five, the wetter
slopes of the Andes being apparently their ancestral home. British botanists
recognise eight or more varieties: here are only the two best known, the
sweet and the common violet.

White violets are sweet. The 'blue' scented violet is much rarer, except in
certain localities. 'Blue' is misleading, for this flower is most often a rich
purple contrasting royally with the orange of its anthers—a bravery of
colour repeated in many plants, in the toadflaxes and the nightshades
especially. The leaf is markedly heart-shaped, and slightly downy on the
underside; like the flower stem it springs singly direct from the root.

Viola odorata is the French Violette de Mars, the German Märzveilchen,
Parkinson's 'choice flower of delight', the 'Black violet' of Gerard. It is this
official variety that has always been employed in the making of medicines,
sweets and cosmetics, which may explain its comparative rarity today.

[1] Edward Thomas: 'But these things also are Spring's.'

Harmless laxatives and emetics are still sometimes made from its leaves, and a 'cure' for cancer infused therefrom. Today its flowers are still candied for confectionery, and of course yield perfume, one of the few flower-extracts which retain the original essence. But for these purposes the larger plants grown abroad are used rather than the 'moist delicious breath of rainy violets'[1] in our wild woods picked by the herbalists and housewifely gentlewomen of past centuries. John Evelyn recommends as 'one of the

Sweet Violet

[1] Ruth Pitter.

most agreeable of all the herbaceous dishes' violet leaves 'at the entrance of Spring fried brownish and eaten with Orange or Lemon Juice and Sugar'. The recipes that have come down to us are naturally the more extravagant ones, for the poorer illiterate folk bequeathed their lore of cooking and healing by word of mouth from generation to generation. Curious prescriptions have survived from the Middle Ages (Henslow):

'For the hemy-greyne [migraine]. Take 1 libra of seyngrene [houseleek] and 1 quartron of mary-goulden, and of violettes a gret hanful, and take a pynte mylke of a woman that berythe a knave childe, that is a mayde y-wedded, and late hem be stamped in a faire morter al togeder rygt smale, and than with the same mylke tempre it up and make a plastre on a fayre lynen clowte, and than ley it on the hole side of the hede; and lat the hede be holde to a gode hote fyre with the plastre ther-on into the tyme the plastre be thurwe hote on his hede, and then with the hete ly doun, reste hym well, and he shall be hole.'

Gerard has a pretty tale of the origin of the Greek name: 'The Grecians did call it Ion because certain nymphs of Ionia gave that floure first to Jupiter. Others say it was called Ion because when Jupiter had turned the young damosell Io, whom he tenderly loved, into a Cow, the earth brought forth this floure for her food.' As for the aesthetic, nay the spiritual values of the flower, they inspire him to poetry:

'The March Violets have a great prerogative above all others, not only because the mind conceiveth a certain pleasure and recreation by smelling and handling those most odoriferous floures, but also for that very many by these violets receive ornament and comely grace; for there be made of them garlands for the head, nose gaies and poesies, which are delightfull to looke on and pleasant to smel to, speaking nothing of their appropriat vertues; yea gardens themselves receive by these the greatest ornament of all, chiefest beauty and most excellent grace, and the recreation of the minde which is taken hereby cannot be but very good and honest; for they admonish and stirre up a man to that which is comely and honest; for flores, through their beauty, variety of colour, and exquisit forme, do bring to a liberall and gentle manly minde, the remembrance of honestie, comlinesse, and all kindes of vertues; for it would be an unseemly and filthy thing . . . for him that doth looke upon and handle faire and beautiful things, to have his mind not faire, but filthy and deformed.'

COMMON VIOLET

Viola riviniana

The common violet is distinguished from the sweet violet by its lack of scent; hence the derogatory name dog violet—confusing, for *V. canina* is the heath violet! Moreover its flowering time is normally a month later, though when the months do not observe the season (and in what year do they all behave according to plan?) this is not a sure guide. Nor is the colour, for the common violet varies amazingly: it may wear the same purple as the scented or it may be a pale slate grey or even strawberry pink. Most often though it is true 'violet', or a pale lilac, delicately pencilled with the dark lines which are the characteristic marking of the lower and two side petals. Like the other blue violets it usually has as honey guides a row of little hairs at the base of the side petals: they are not found on the white variety.

The violet flower is remarkable for its structure, which is specially designed to prevent self-pollination. The bee is guided to the spur, where nectar lies at the base of two of the stamens. But it must first pass the stigma, which has a small valve that admits pollen carried from the last flower the bee visited, but rejects any brushed from its own anthers by the bee's tongue as it is withdrawn, satisfied, from the spur. However, like the wood sorrel, the violet falls back on self-pollination as a last resort, and for this purpose provides, later in the season, shut buds which germinate within their closed cases, producing seed copiously, whereas for some reason cross-pollination has little result. The fruit too is interesting: when ripe it explosively and audibly shoots out its seeds to a surprising distance.

The leaves of the common violet are more triangular than the sweet violet's, and less the shape of a wide Valentine heart. But the two plants differ chiefly in their habit of growth. The sweet violet rises straight from the root on a single stalk, the 'dog' violet often from freely branching stems; so that if one makes a bunch of each kind, always picking stalks as long as possible, the bunch of common violets is elegant, naturalistic, spreading, looking in its pot just as it grew. The sweet violets make a tight little nosegay, the conventional posy, concentrated purple; the leaves, if any, deliberately arranged, as in Dürer's drawing, in an outer circle.

E

65

Common Violet

GROUND IVY

Glechoma hederacea

If the 'first white violet' proves to be merely bird-dropping or snail-shell, the 'first blue violet' as like as not will be ground ivy, at a distance the deeper colour of sweet rather than of dog violet, the blue of the flowers empurpled by the dye of stems and leaves. Its habitat, as the many variants of 'Gill-by-the-hedge' names show, is on sunny banks as often as woodland glades, and I have even found it covering a whole field. It must be this creeping habit rather than the kidney or heart shape of its leaves that suggests ivy, a 'signature' shape that may account for some of its uses in medicine, both ancient (the Greek name *glechoma* referring to mint or thyme) and numerous, for medicine runs in the labiate family.

I once found myself the only occupant of a country bus except for three Romany-speaking gipsies, who proffered artificial flowers for sale. This opened up conversation, in which I asked what herbs they used. 'Ground ivy' they began immediately, but before I could elicit more they had unfortunately reached their stop. It seems to have been a useful tonic for many a complaint, 'when all other remedies have failed' says Mrs. Grieve ambiguously. Gerard, who saw the blue flowers 'gaping like little hoods', is emphatic: 'For any griefe whatsoever in the eyes, yea, although the sight were nighhand gone, it is proved to be the best medicine in the world.'

It had a more general and popular use, namely in beer brewing, right up to the reign of Henry VIII, and afterwards. In the sixteenth century it began to be superseded commercially by hops introduced from Flanders, which not only flavoured but preserved, the Flemish name *hoppe* replacing the native *hymele*, and the old word 'ale-hoof' (Anglo-Saxon *hofe*, ground ivy) disappearing with its use. Home brewers may have bought from the Cherry Girl, whose old street ballad runs:

> Sweet cowslips I cry and ground ivy I sell,
> And round about London am known mighty well,
> But when my sweet cowslips no longer abound
> I cry my sweet cherries a penny a pound.

67

Ground ivy has two peculiarities, neither of which appears to have a purpose. One is that besides the 'little hoods' it produces much smaller and virtually stamenless flowers. The other, as the pedantic authoress of *Conversations in Botany* (1823) tells her hapless child Edward, is that the strong aromatic herbal scent is on the underside of the leaf only. It is somehow comforting to know that plants have not yet yielded up all their secrets.

Ground Ivy

WOOD ANEMONE

Anemone nemorosa

Surely there can be no more lyrical name for any wild flower than *Anemone nemorosa*. The music must have helped to preserve 'anemone' as the common name 'windflower' the translation of (*anemone*), perhaps a time-of-flowering name like 'Easter flower' and 'Cuckoo flower', for it is from the middle of windy March till early April that its white stars drift through the woods—the Italian name is 'Star flower'. So fragile is it, scarcely standing the picking, that it would fare ill exposed to an equinoctial gale, and chooses to grow under trees (hence *nemorosa*) that give shelter yet, still leafless, let in the sunlight.

The anemones are already there at the beginning of March, but it is only if you have been staring at the ground for a while, wishing they were out, that you become aware of something different in texture rather than in colour from the dark earth—the coppery-olive leaves curling over to protect the young plant. When they unfurl they cover all the ground with a beautiful filigree tracery, the three leaves meeting round the stem to make hexagons patterned like snow crystals. From the centre rises the flower, a white six-pointed star with a golden circle of stamens around green pistils in the midst. The star is formed not of petals but of sepals which (since there are no nectaries but only pollen to attract insects) give protection with the rosy tinge at their base as the head bends over at night and in rain.

The flowers vary considerably: whole colonies among the stretches of white may be deep pink all over, violet, or nearly crimson; others are smaller and greenish (perhaps virus-infected?) while seven- or eight-pointed stars are not uncommon. As April turns to May they begin to droop and fold, the golden centres turn to green and then to fruits as pretty as the related Pasque flower's though much smaller, while the early leaves on the stem have been succeeded by true and larger leaves straight from the underground rhizome.

No plant so easily found and seen could have escaped being exploited by man for the usual cures, but as in most of the Ranunculus family the juice is acrid and poisonous, and it is no longer used medicinally.

E*

Wood Anemone

GREATER STITCHWORT

Stellaria holostea

I always think it is the first warm sun of spring that brings out the sudden galaxy of stitchwort stars, in hedgerows rather than in woodland, though there too. How could such promise have crept unawares on eyes that were hungry for any sign of the end of winter? Only because the thin leaves and pale fragile straggling stems alone could have been taken for grass unless one was diligently searching. And what a white! whiter than milk, silky of texture, bright as moonlight; Edward Thomas's 'whitest flower on earth'.

Its many names reflect all these things—cuckoo names for the April flowering, button names for its size and starry shape (five or ten points to the circle according to whether the petals are seen as double or as deeply cleft), adder names (and hence supersititious names) for its love of sunny banks, smock, snow and moon names for its whiteness. 'Stitchwort' seems to be a translation of *holostea*, 'whole bone', originally applied to it by mistake and perpetuating its supposed powers of healing fractures and cramp.

The centre of the star varies as spring advances: first the inner and later the outer ring of yellow stamens stands erect, and when both have faded the green stigmas curl outwards over them. With three methods—cross-pollination, fertilisation by insects using each flower's own pollen on its own stigmas, and mechanical self-fertilisation—the plant deserves to propagate well, and its success is shown later by the liberal sprinkling of little green balls full of rattling seed that show where the constellations once shone.

Cuckoo-pint and Greater Stitchwort

YELLOW STAR OF BETHLEHEM

Gagea lutea

Gagea, after Sir Thomas Gage (1781-1820), English botanist of greengage fame, is an ugly name for so fair a thing as the Yellow Star of Bethlehem. No word thus artificially created from a name can sound right for a flower, either euphonically or ethically: it is all of a piece with the arrogant assumption that plants were made solely for the use or for the delectation of man, and are his property, to be uprooted, 'naturalised'—what a misnomer!—or patronised as it may please him.

It is very rare. Smith in Sowerby's *English Botany* says 'Near Oxford it has been found plentifully, and in some parts of Yorkshire,' and Gerard mentions 'Somersetshire, in the cornfields'—was he thinking of the White Star of Bethlehem, *Ornithogalum umbellatum*, found more usually now in gardens? The first sight of it is unforgettable. It is early April, the kind of day when the wind still has ice in it and yet the sun shines hot in the lee of the trees, where dog violets cover the bank. The chiffchaff, newly arrived, sings with laborious persistence. The hanger slopes steeply down to the slow stream, so steeply that one has to cling to the hazels to keep one's footing. At first one sees only young bluebell shoots among the dead oak leaves. And then a group of stars shines out of this sombre background, then another, and from there almost to the edge of the water below stretches a constellation, nowhere thickly clustered—for not all plants flower every year, nor do they often set seed—but patterning the ground all over.

The flower is very like those that dot the foreground of Florentine paintings—frail, vivid in colour, perfect in symmetry and crisp in detail. The umbel holds only two, three or four finely pointed stars. The metallic gold of the curled petals brims over the edges, outlining the green beneath. But should one visit the wood after midday they have all apparently vanished as if by magic, for these stars set at noon: the flowers close into green buds, giving no hint of their exquisite form and lustre. As each begins to fade the green becomes more and more insistent until no trace of gold is left: it is just a small green lily standing beside its single green blade.

73

Yellow Star of Bethlehem

BUTCHER'S BROOM

Ruscus aculeatus

Butcher's Broom is a rather repellent plant: stiff, angular, spiky (*aculeatus*), and of so uniform a green—a harsh, dark, acid green—that it might have been dyed for a flower-arranger's decoration. This indeed is said to have been one of its uses, ornamenting the butcher's Christmas joints, though perhaps the purpose was more practical, the spines at the tips of its leaves— cruel enough to have earned the name 'butcher's' anyway—keeping mice off the meat. Tied in a bundle the hard woody stems may have made him a broom; or is the name from the the genista broom, not unlike *Ruscus aculeatus* in stiff growth and dark green colour?

The preference for the name 'knee-holly' (knee-height evergreen? or bone-setter?) by earlier herbalists and their continual recommendations of the plant as a diuretic seem to point to these two uses as reliable, in contrast to a 'Leechdom' against the 'drop' and the 'maw', whatever they were. It would surely have taken a whole bushful to yield the two cupfuls of juice, mingled with honey and taken fasting, prescribed for the complaints.

Butcher's Broom is a peculiar plant in many ways. It is our only *Ruscus,* and our only shrub and evergreen in the Liliaceae family. It is hardy enough to flower in December and January, and where you once saw it you are likely to see it indefinitely, yet it is not found wild north of the Midlands. The 'leaves' are technically 'cladodes', and fiercely prickly though they are, the soft young shoots were sometimes eaten as asparagus, with which there is some affinity. There may be one or two flowers, male or female, but only one flourishes at a time, lying as if blown onto the surface of the 'leaf'. Though tiny they are pretty—three-petalled, greenish-white, with violet stamens or stigmas. Against their shrubby evergreen background they perhaps bear enough resemblance to myrtle to justify the name 'Jew's myrtle'—Turner's *Myrtus sylvestris*. By September the female flower has become a large single berry, scarlet and spherical, looking as if someone has stuck it there on purpose, and despite its size miraculously staying put.

But the strangest phenomenon of this odd plant is that death transforms it into a thing of beauty. Bleached to a skeleton, luminous and ghostly, the branching form now seen single and clearly delineated, the attenuated transparent leaves a network of fine veins, it seems the living spirit of the dark and sinister shrub buried in the hedge.

Butcher's Broom

WOOD SORREL

Oxalis acetosella

Few plants possess more names than the wood sorrel. Most of them, in most languages, refer to its acidity, for it yields a quantity of oxalic acid, once used to make salts of lemon: Salt cellar, Sour Sally, Sauerklee, La Surelle, Oseille de Bois—Oseille from the Greek *oxus*, acid, via Latin *oxalis*. Other names emphasise its edible quality: Hare's meat, Cuckoo's meat, God Almighty's bread and cheese, bread and cheese and cider. Country people use 'bread and cheese' to describe anything eatable, whatever the taste—children give the name to the young leaves of the hawthorn—but 'cider' hints at the tartness as well. 'Cuckoo's meat' shows the time of flowering, like another name found also in Italian, French, Spanish and German—'Alleluia', for it was between Easter and Whitsun that Psalms 113-117, which end with 'Alleluia', were sung in the Church services. It occurs, oddly spelt, in fifteenth-century manuscripts, and the plant appears in Italian paintings of the period. 'Luzula', the name of the conserve formerly made from the sugared leaves ('an agreeably acid refreshing conserve' as described in Sowerby, 'partaking of the flavour of green tea') seems to be 'Juliola', a corruption of Alleluia. It is not surprising that wood sorrel has been called Wild Shamrock and Good Luck: the German Sauerklee and the Dutch Klaverzuurung also allude to its triple leaf. 'Stubwort' shows its habitat—around the 'stubs' of trees—and Fairy bells, like Sleeping Beauty, the fragility of the flower and its propensity for hanging its head except when the sun shines, so that it is more often closed and pendulous than erect and open.

Flower, leaf, stalk and root, it is the daintiest of woodland plants. It is found by its leaves rather than its flowers, partly because of their bold trefoil shape and still more because of the freshness of their yellow-green, bright as though the April sun had penetrated the shady patch of wood they cover. They are soft with silvery silky hairs, and extremely sensitive, even to touch—at night, in rain, and during dull weather they are folded back like butterfly wings. The underside is often bright reddish purple that also flushes both blade and midrib, and then the light shining through the superimposed colours of the upper and under surfaces turns them olive-green or copper. The frail flower rises from the root on a single slender stalk, pink or purple; its five white petals, tinged with yellow at the base, are delicately pencilled in lilac—'some brightnes of carnation' (Gerard). The 'carnation' dyes not only petal, stalk and leaf, but also the tiny bracts halfway up the flower-stem, and even the root—'coral-root' is another of its names.

The wood sorrel has two kinds of flowers to ensure cross-pollination, but lest this should fail it produces, like the violet, tiny round buds which pollinate themselves without opening. The fruits are enclosed in a case so elastic that in late summer they eject their shiny seeds at a touch.

The old herbalists put wood sorrel to many uses. It was compounded with some fifty other herbs to make a 'save'. 'Save ys a drynke that wol hele al maner wounde without plaister or ani outher selve. Hit ys the beste drynke that ys for a wondid man' (Henslow). Boiled in milk or in the form of syrup it quenched the thirst; it was employed as a gargle, as a salve, and what modern medicine might describe as 'a valuable source of Vitamin C'. The Devon name 'Green sauce' confirms Gerard's advice: 'Sorrell du Bois stamped and used for greene sauce is good for them that have sicke and feeble stomackes; for it strengthneth the stomacke, procureth appetite, and of all Sorrell sauces is the best, not onely in vertue but also in the pleasantness of his taste.' Sir Kenelm Digby (1669) gives a not unattractive recipe for 'an excellent and wholesome Watergruel with woodsorrel and currents: Into a posset of two quarts of water, besides the due proportion of beaten oat-meal, put two handfuls of wood-sorrel a little chopped and bruised, and a good quantity of picked and washed currents, tyed loosely in a thin stuff bag (as a bolter cloth). Boil these very well together, seasoning the Composition in due time; with salt nutmeg Mace, or what else you please, as Rosemary etc. When it is sufficiently boiled strain the Oat-meal and press out all the Juyce and humidity of the Currants and Herbs, throwing away the insipid husks; and season it with Sugar and Butter; and to each Porrenger-full two spoonfuls of Rhenish Wine, and the Yolke of an Egg.'

Wood Sorrel

WILD STRAWBERRY
Fragaria vesca

Britain is poorly off for edible wild fruits—no wonder the Anglo-Saxon word *aeppel* had to do duty for fruit of any kind. At their best blackberries and bilberries are excellent, but raspberries stay in the north, where they are rare enough, while crab, sloe, hip and barberry are uneatable unless in jelly and wine. So the strawberry, which will grow anywhere except in the tropics and Arctic Circle, in plain and on mountain, easily takes the prize for juiciness, richness of colour, and above all for delicacy of flavour and scent: *fragaria* like its French name *fraise* comes from the Latin *fragare*, 'to smell'.

Since it likes the shady heart of a wood it has some protection from pickers. John Aubrey writes 'Strawberries in Colern woods' (ploughed in the 1939-45 war!) 'exceeding plentiful; the earth is not above two inches above the freestone. The poore chidren gather them and sell them to Bathe, but they kill the young ashes by barking them, to make boxes to put them in.' H. J. Massingham describes a Gloucestershire wood with 'so many that a hunted outlaw could have lived on their fruit for a week and been filled.'

Both their permanence and their increase are due to their runners, spreading like those of our garden strawberry—which however has been bred not from our native wild plant but from a cross with the American variety introduced in the seventeenth century, losing in subtlety of taste what it has gained in size. Runners are one of the distinctions between the edible (*vesca*) and the barren strawberry, which is very like it, but keeps its creeping stems underground, spreading above them over banks and hedge-rows, while the wild strawberry stands erect. Barren strawberry is relegated to the status of *Potentilla sterile,* or *fragariastrum,* the derogatory *astrum* referring to its uselessness as food, for it has a fruit sufficient for its own purposes of reproduction. Moreover the wild strawberry, which comes a little later in the spring, avoiding the worst frosts, is larger in both flower and leaf than the barren. Nor is size the only difference. Both flowers have the charming pattern of a Tudor rose, with sepals forming a green star whose tips peep between the white star of the petals; but barren strawberry petals are heart-shaped, while the wild strawberry's curve outwards in a bracket shape. Wild strawberry leaves have a brighter and shinier surface, the three pleated lobes with regularly indented edges meeting symmetrically in the centre, whereas the top leaflet of the barren strawberry's triangle is parted from the other two by a very short stem.

Wild Strawberry

'Ther is a juice pressed out of strawberries whiche by continuance of tyme encreaseth in strength,' says Turner, 'and that is a present [immediate] remedy against the sores and wheales of the face and against blodshoten eyes'. Parkinson says it is 'good for the passions of the heart caused by the perturbation of the spirits, being eyther drunk alone or in wyne; and maketh the heart merry.' *The Language of Flowers* (1835) records that Linnaeus cured himself of gout with the fruit, and 'used to desire his servant to purchase all that were brought to the door, and daily ate large numbers of them' (Anne Pratt). The leaves also were used, both externally and internally. In seventeenth- and eighteenth-century cookery nearly every recipe for drinks uses strawberry leaves—said to have a special odour when pressed—with such plants as woodruff and violet leaves.

Fantastic explanations have been given for the name. Thomas Tusser's doggerel verse 'Good Points of Husbandry' (1557) describes the use of straw to protect the plants in winter:

> If frost do continue, take this for a law,
> The strawberries look to be covered with straw,
> Laid overly trim upon crotches and bows,
> And after uncovered, as weather allows.

But the Anglo-Saxon *streawbyrige* comes from the time before wild strawberries were brought from the autumn woods into gardens for the special cultivation set out in the same treatise (September):

> The barberry, respis and gooseberry too
> Look now to be planted, as other things do.
> The gooseberry, respis, and roses, all three,
> With strawberries under them, trimly agree.
>
> . . .
>
> Wife into the garden, and set me a plot
> Of strawberry rootes, of the best to be got,
> Such growing abroad among thorns in the wood,
> Well chosen and picked, prove excellent good.

Anglo-Saxon uses *streaw* to translate the Biblical 'mote' in the eye, surely in the context the smallest of flecks, such as the tiny seeds 'strewn' over the soft crimson surface of this most delicious of wild fruits.

TOOTHWORT
Lathraea squamaria

There is no mistaking toothwort. Its repulsive appearance would lead one to decide that it outraged the plant decencies. It is a parasite, and is often found clustering round the 'stowls' of the budding hazels on whose decayed roots it battens. It makes no chlorophyll, that green transformer of sunlight, and rises the colour of naked flesh from its bed of dark humus. Instead of green leaves it has uncommonly large bracts, one at the base of each flower, and, lurking on the underground stem, scales like human teeth. So it is named 'concealed, scaly'—*lathraea squamaria*, and likewise in modern languages— in German Schuppenwurz (scalewort), in Portuguese Dentaria bastarda, in French La Clandestine. Worse still, the 'teeth' are hollow, and incarcerate small insects which it is rumoured the plant devours. It is cold and clammy to the touch, and its flowers, perpetually hooded in hairy four-sepalled calyxes whence the purple stigmas protrude like tongues, grow down one side of the stem only; lay it sideways and you see ranged the fleshy udders of a white sow. In the whole woodland there is nothing like it except broomrape, to which it is nearly akin, and bird's-nest orchid, and these are swarthy and lean. It is of no use to either man or beast.

Yet there is great beauty in this odd plant, in the regular growth of the buds on the stem, like crockets up a spire, in the orchid-like form of its flower, upper lip arched in a hood, lower lip three-cleft and hanging, and in the variety of its colours. Milkwhite or creamy yellow, it is luminous as mushrooms at dusk; faded to a light cocoa-brown it is scarcely to be distinguished from the withered leaves where it grows. You may find a pinkish colony of every shade from flesh-tint to purple, beneath a sycamore tree whose rosy scales lie scattered around it. And should you pick a young plant and hold it where the sunlight can strike full on the bracts behind the stem you will see them suddenly transformed to gleaming shells of mother-of-pearl.

83

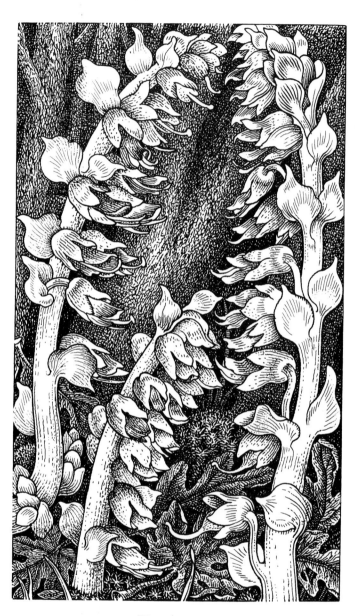

Toothwort

RAMSONS

Allium ursinum

A narrow lane with steep banks winds down between hazel copses into a wooded valley. It is the second week in May, and the cuckoo is calling. Suddenly the air is redolent with the fresh nostalgic odour of all the springs that ever were. Sure enough, up the bank and spilling all over the wood are the starry snow-crystal hemispheres of ramsons—wild garlic.

No plant is more beautiful. At first the bud is enfolded in a fine semi-transparent twofold sheath that rustles like paper at a touch, parting at last to show as many as two dozen white six-pointed stars clustered in an umbel, the golden stamens, three longer, three shorter, often marking a triangle within the star. The leaves, easily mistaken for lily-of-the-valley before the flowers are out, silken-sheened and the clear green colour of young beech, rise and fall like waves in the most graceful curves.

No flower could make a visually more exquisite bridal bouquet, except perhaps ground elder, another lovely umbel, and for a different reason equally despised. There's the rub: all depends whether you like or loathe garlic. Sides are taken with passion, mostly it must be admitted against, as various names like 'Stinking flower' show. *Allium ursinum* is 'bear's garlic'—inferior, like 'Poor man's garlic' and 'Gipsy's gibbles', for in comparison with true garlic the root is but one poor thin bulb and rootlets. 'The scent thereof be somewhat valient and offensive' writes Turner. According to Sowerby it 'infects the air around'. Mrs. Grieve gives warning of the 'evil smell. Many woods, especially in the Cotswold Hills, are spots to be avoided when it is in flower'. 'Not pleasing to British nostrils' admits Edward Step, though Gerard thought it might be eaten by 'such as are of a strong constitution, and labouring men'. Even animals shared the prejudice; if it was put into mole-holes they were said to 'come out presently' (i.e. immediately) 'as amazed' (stupefied). Sheep refused it; cows and hens were kept from it lest the flavour should taint milk and eggs. On the other hand the Egyptians invoked it as a deity, and the Greeks placed it at crossroads as a propitiatory offering to Hecate. Dumas wrote of Provence as

F*

85

'particularly perfumed by the refined essence of this mystically attractive bulb'. Tennyson makes his lotus-eaters lie luxuriously 'propped on beds of amaranth and moly', moly being a yellow garlic. Was he another enthusiast, or had his botany for once let him down?

To the Anglo-Saxons it was simply *hramsa*, plural *hramsan*, whatever they meant by that, the places where it grew, like Ramsdale, noted not romantically for their spring beauty but practically for the 'poor man's triacle', the valued remedy for numerous complaints internal and external. An old rhyme ran:

> Eat leeks in March and Ramsons in May
> And all the year after physicians may play.

It defeated infections, especially as a poultice for suppurating wounds, a 'folk' cure for which was merely to hang onions in the patient's room to absorb the poison as he lost it. For a fourteenth century recipe: 'Take bran and the taylis [roots?] of garloc and do thereto red wyn, and put hit in a newe erthyn pot that was never usyed, and let boyle a boyling, and thenne take hit over the fyre, and make a playster thereof and lay hit al hot to thy sore as hot as thou myght sofre' (Henslow).

Ramsons

LESSER PERIWINKLE

Vinca minor

Ther sprang the violete al newe
And fresshe pervinke, rich of hewe

—by the wells in the garden of Chaucer's *Romaunt of the Rose*.

Through primrose tufts in that sweet bower
The periwinkle trailed its wreaths

around Wordsworth in early spring, and in the path of Edward Thomas:

There once the walls
Of the ruined cottage stood.
The periwinkle crawls
With flowers in its hair into the wood.

In flowerless hours
Never will the bank fail,
With everlasting flowers
On fragments of blue plates, to tell the tale.

(*A Tale*)

Poetry, romance, mediaeval tapestries and the William Morris designs of closely intertwined flower and leaf they inspired, lore and legend, childhood memories, all come to the mind at the sight of this lovable flower—and memories first. The windmill shape, as if the petals, cut at an angle, were whirling round the central star, reminds me of the paper 'windmills' handed to us as children by the rag-and-bone man in fair exchange, spinning at the top of their sticks the faster as we ran off gleefully with our prizes. Only these were four-pointed, the swastika shape that was then still innocent. Periwinkle too is occasionally four-petalled, but five is the true and prettier pattern. The twist of the opened flower seems to have been set going already in the bud furled like an umbrella.

88

Lesser Periwinkle

It is rather the blue of dog violets, soft and slightly greyed, than the brighter colour suggested by its names 'Blue-eyed beauty', 'Blue star', 'Blue Betsy'. Gardeners have produced many variations—the flowers may be truly deep blue, rich purple with narrow petals, completely double, wine-red, white-streaked as if by crossing, and pure white, and some have conspicuously variegated leaves.

There is some doubt as to whether periwinkle is strictly wild, for despite complicated arrangements for cross-fertilisation it does not set seed in this country, nor with such strong rooting runners does it need to. Greater periwinkle was certainly introduced, and from a warmer clime: it is kin to oleander! Greater and lesser differ not only in size of flower and length of stem but in their sepals, the first's long and hairy, the other's short and smooth.

Wandering among periwinkle one is continually caught in a man-trap of looped stems, how rightly called fetters (Latin *vincula*): in one West Country name 'winkles' have become 'cockles'! It is easy to see how those long twines could lend themselves to the weaving of wreaths, and that all the year round; it may have been introduced by the Romans for this purpose. Was it the binding quality which suggested its use as a love charm? 'Perwynke when it is beate into powder with worms of ye earth wrapped about it and with an herbe called houslyke, it induceth love between man and wyfe if it be used in their meales.'[1] As it was also thought to 'bind' blood it was used to stop haemorrhage; but the name 'Sorcerer's violet' reveals an older and more magical tradition of the herb as a panacea: 'This wort avails well for many things, that is first against devil sicknesses and against adders and against wild beasts and against poisons and against envy and against fear, and that thou mayest have grace, and if thou hast this wort with thee thou art blessed and ever prosperous. Thou shalt take the wort saying thus: I pray thee, vinca pervinca, thee that art to be had for thy many useful qualities, that thou come to me glad, blossoming and with thy virtues, that thou so equip me that I may be safe and ever happy, undamaged by poisons and by wrath. When thou wilt take the wort thou shalt be clear from every uncleanness. And thou shalt take it when the moon is 9 nights old and 11 nights and 13 nights and 30 nights and when it is one night old' (Cockayne, trans. Apuleius Herbarium, printed 1480).

[1] *The Boke of Secretes of Albartus Magnus, of the Vertues of Herbs, Stones and Certaine Beastes,* quot. Mrs. Grieve.

ARCHANGEL

Galeobdolon luteum

Sometimes in the heart of a bluebell wood in May the sea of blue is suddenly interrupted by spires of honey gold—that beautiful dead nettle, yellow archangel. Nor is it only the colour contrast that is sharp but the stance of the plant, so upright, so aspiring among the downward curves of the weighted bluebells around it.

All three 'nettles', white, red, and yellow, are popularly called 'dead', 'dumb', 'deaf' and so on because their leaves though nettle-like are stingless; and as all three are also named Archangel the epithet 'yellow' (*luteum*) has to be the distinguishing word. Sophisticated though archangel sounds, it goes back at least as far as the seventeenth century in common parlance, though it is not easily explained. May 8th may be officially St. Michael's day, but it is at Michaelmas rather than in May that he is remembered. Now the white dead nettle is often still in bloom as late in the year; indeed there is scarcely a month when that flower is nowhere to be found. Was it perhaps the first of the dead nettles to owe its name to the archangel?

Yellow archangel is characteristically a flower of May and even before it blooms the darker green and narrow form of its leaves distinguish it from the common white dead nettle. The upper petal, hooding the stamens protectively, has exactly and designedly the curve of an alighting humble bee, though popular imagination sees it as a weasel's head poised alertly on stretched-up neck, and calls it 'weasel-snout'. The Greek name, *Galeobdolon*, means 'weasel-stink', a libel.

At this stage, tightly curled, the buds are round and luminous as pearls, creamy, greenish or golden. Flower unfurled, the delicate red-brown markings on the lower petals are revealed, and the crimson of the stigma, echoed in the base of the corolla tube where the nectar lies. Even after flowering the plant is still beautiful, for the five long sharp points of the calyx bells ranged round the stem hold in their depths shining green fruits marked into four nutlets like little 'farl' loaves or hot cross buns. These when ripe eject their seeds far and wide, but the plant spreads more easily by

91

creeping rootstock, a habit exploited by nurserymen who sell the handsome variegated kind as evergreen ground cover. In a garden it will keep even ground elder at bay awhile, and having spread in all directions over the soil likes nothing better than to climb any shrub it encounters. The wild archangel is never so vigorous, and in many localities is rare.

The Greek name, *lamios,* 'throat' (used by Linnaeus), refers to the shape of the corolla tube, not to the medicinal use, which was mainly, as of other labiates such as woundwort, to staunch blood. Culpeper suggests sarcastically that the name Archangel was given by physicians 'to put a gloss upon their practice'. Was he thinking of Gerard's attractive recipe?: 'The flowers are baked with suger as roses are, as also the distilled water of them, which is used to make the heart merry, to make a good colour in the face, and to refresh the vitall spirits.' More likely he is referring to its supposed cure for the king's evil, scurvy, for which a dose of almost any non-poisonous greenstuff would have been more likely to help than being touched by royalty.

Archangel

BLUEBELL

Endymion nonscriptus

For a picture of a typical English spring most would choose a bluebell wood in May. The wife of Hamada, the Japanese potter, used to come every year expressly for this enchanting sight, as we might go to Japan for a feast of cherry blossom. 'Sheet' of blue, however hackneyed, is the word: the entire wood is carpeted. But it is a living blue, made vibrant by the green of juicy stem and narrow curving leaf, by the varying shades of the flowers—some dark violet, some so pale as to be almost the grey of the beech trunks around, a few white—by a deeper reddish purple on the petals and the two little bracts at their base, and by the clashing chalky yellow of the anthers. All the graceful heads curve over in the same direction, weighted down with their rows of bells. Near the path a single plant has the chance to show how it really grows, the stem rising from a spread star of leaves. Overhead slender beech twigs are breaking into fresh green, while a rain of black pollen patters down from the golden oak catkins. Over the blue floor wriggles a coppery-green shoot of young black bryony, like a snake and snake-coloured. A cuckoo flies stuttering after his hen, who answers with her underwater gurgle.

Children can go mad in a bluebell wood. The lust of possession comes over them, and caring nought on this occasion for starry anemones or spikes of early purple orchids they concentrate on bluebells, picking them till the sticky stems creak together in their hot hands, pulling up white understems and all in their search for ever bigger, better and bluer specimens, which they soon find tend to grow together in patches. I once found thirty-four flowers on a single stem, counting unopened buds at the tip and those already in fat triangular fruit at the bottom; but twelve is a good average. At last it takes two small arms to hold the heavy drooping bunch, and picking stops perforce.

Fortunately this vandalism appears to have done less than the anticipated harm through the non-conservation-conscious years. The destruction of woodland has been the worst culprit, for bluebells love the dappled shade of young leaves, and themselves need their full quota of untrampled leaves to

Bluebell

nourish the bulb. But where the wood has remained, so as a rule have the bluebells, at least since the sixteenth century, before which there is no record of them here, while on the Continent they are not found east of Italy. For this is not the Greek hyacinth of legend, nor even the delicate little white Roman hyacinth of bulb bowls, though that is far more like our wild flower than the coarser garden bluebell, *Endymion hispanica,* and we may perhaps be forgiven for thinking ours specially native.

'Bluebell' is so inevitable a name that it has superseded the local names— the 'blue' and 'cuckoo' and 'fairy' names, and others like 'griggles' and 'crowflower' that sound as if folk christened plants with the first syllables that came into their heads. Latin names are often no more apposite: *Hyacinthus nonscriptus* ('not written on') means unmarked with the letters AI, the cry of woe for the death of Hyacinth, but has anyone ever seen any hyacinth so inscribed? *Scilla nutans* ('nodding') is more satisfactory.

The slimy sap of the bluebell was used as starch for ruffs and as glue for bookbinding in Elizabethan times, but its omission from the earliest medical treatises ensured its exemption from the usual herb-hunting, and its survival to gladden our hearts today.

EARLY PURPLE ORCHID

Orchis mascula

This is the earliest of all British orchids to flower, twayblade soon following, and these two are also the most common and widespread. Early purple is moreover the most distinguished in colour, its rich magenta splashed like its leaves with spots of darker dye, contrasting strikingly yet harmoniously with the bluebells among which it often grows.

A strange family, the orchids, maybe a branch of Liliaceae which seems to have converted a potentially malignant growth into a mutual necessity: orchids depend for their food on the presence of a mycorrhizal fungus in the woods (often beech) on chalk or limestone soil where they grow. This means they are virtually impossible to transplant, and take many years to start flowering, which is perhaps why they have gone to great lengths—almost as if controlled by human intelligence—to ensure cross-pollination, even twisting the stem to present the two anthers in exactly the right position to brush the entering bee with their pollen.

Their complicated flowers look sinister. It is easy to see why Culpeper so disliked them, saying that Nature had played the fool with them. Perhaps it was their suggestion of magical powers that led the curious to dig them up. And here was the Doctrine of Signatures indeed—the double-tubered testicles-like root indicated beyond doubt an aphrodisiac. The firmer of the tubers (which actually stores food for next year) would excite lust, the slacker (which supplies the current year) would allay it; the first would cause the begetting or conception of males, the other of females. The botanical names *orchis* (Greek 'testicle') and *mascula* announce this quality twice over; the earlier term *Satyrion* perpetuates those legendary pursuers of nymphs; and popular names like 'dog stones', 'fox stones', 'bull's bags', 'hare ballocks' and Anglo-Saxon *beallocwyrt* echo the tradition.

Mercifully this aphrodisiac, unlike many, was edible. The Arab word for 'dog stones' became in English 'salep' or 'saloop', a very digestible and nutritious concoction something like slippery elm, made from the tubers of early purple and other orchids imported from Persia and Turkey and also

G

97

grown in this country. Charles Lamb (who however confuses salep with the sassafras used to flavour it) mentions a tavern in Fleet Street advertised as 'the only Salopian house in London'. The humbler street stall was more in the poor chimney-sweeps' line, and there Lamb begs his readers to treat them to a bowlful, suggesting that the mucilage soothed the 'fuliginous concretions' in their sore mouths.

At least it filled them—an ounce to half a gallon of water was said to suffice for a daily ration, and the sailing ships of the day always carried some in reserve.

Early Purple Orchid

TWAYBLADE

Listera ovata

The name is from Dr. Martin Lister, physician to Queen Anne; *ovata* describes the shape of the leaves.

With early purple, this is the commonest of British orchids; we even have it in our own lawn, come from nowhere. 'Twayblade' would suit no other orchid except the butterfly, and then much less well. For Gerard, whose description is irresistible, it was Herbe Bifoile, 'in the middle whereof are placed in comely order two broad leaves, ribbed and chamfered, in shape like the leaves of Plantaine. Upon the top of the stalke groweth a slender greenish spike made of many small floures, each little floure resembling a gnat, or little gosling newly hatched.' It is of another orchid, but it could well be of twayblade, that he writes 'the floures having hanging out of everie one as it were the body of a little man . . . with arms stretched forth, and thighs stradling abroad.'

He calls the stem 'tender, fat, and full of juice'. It is sticky all over, being expressly designed to catch insects. Those too small to be of use to the plant are prevented from climbing up the stem, while larger ones, chiefly ichneumon, are rewarded with a sweet drink. Sated, raising their heads for flight, they rub the stamens, the pollen thus firmly fixed to their bodies with the same glue!

As if to make doubly sure of fertilisation the plant has a long flowering season. Already in April the first appearance is a woodland floor of closely furled old-fashioned sweet packets that gradually gape to reveal two leaves holding a miniature corn-on-the-cob of buds. In early May, the stalks rising, they look more like asparagus. By the end of July, now a foot or even two feet high, still in bloom or fruiting, they hold maybe as many as sixty little yellow-green men, each dancing on his short stem.

Although twayblade takes fourteen years to produce flowers, building up food from its special underground fungus, it is well enough established to flourish even on sour soils (although it prefers lime), and everywhere except in Scotland and the extreme north of England. In compensation Scotland has

100

Twayblade

the lesser twayblade, not found elsewhere, which is so small that one has to part the heather to find it.

Of British orchids, only twayblade and early purple had medicinal uses. The green flowers of twayblade no doubt accounted for its inclusion in a balsam for 'green' wounds, according to Gerard's experience with 'good success'. Was it those opening pairs of leaves that prompted its application to ruptures and 'burstings'?

OXLIP

Primula elatior

Now anemone flowers are beginning to give place to heads of pale hooked fruits, and tiny clinging balls hang from the dog's mercury, whose leaves have grown into a low unbroken forest, till at a distance the only brown earth to be seen is the narrow footpath. The monotony beguiles one into a steady, indifferent tread . . . suddenly arrested by stumbling on something close by the track—an uncanny, witchy thing like a domed sponge. The next second comes recognition: this is the luscious morel, prized by gourmets above the mushroom; and where there is one there should be more, for they grow always where fires have burnt in forest clearings, and unlike most fungi they flourish in the spring. More there are: some pale fawn, some darkest of browns; some large, some small; some perfectly formed, some misshapen.

The search has led imperceptibly into a way seldom chosen. The morels—there were not so many after all—stop as abruptly as they began, but the hunt is hardly abandoned when, also nearly in the footway, there rises a handsome head of luminous yellow flowers. A late freak primrose, showing its polyanthus form above ground? The botanist might say so, for he has decided that the true oxlip is a native of the eastern counties only. But this is a day of discovery, for though far from home it answers all the oxlip tests. Its flowers all face the same way, more primrose than cowslip in having no crimson spots at the centre. Smaller than those of the primrose but larger than the cowslip's, they have neither the fresh pale green of the one nor the rich gold of the other, and their scent is but a faint compromise between the two perfumes. The leaves narrow suddenly at the waist as do the cowslip's, but they are part and parcel of the plant, unlike the cowslip's small flattened rosette, which seems to lead an independent, forgotten existence safe from grazing animals on the field floor. Here are five flowers on a tall green stem like a cowslip's (*elatior* means 'taller'), while a few steps away is a plant with still larger flowers on a rosy stem like a primrose's and no more oxlips are to be found today.

103

Oxlip

RED CAMPION

Melandrium rubrum

Of all its names Edward Thomas's Lob's 'Bridget-in-her bravery' really fits it, even if almost too good to be true—that bright feminine pink, flaunted so extravagantly in moist bank or woodland border. Other names: 'cuckoo flower', 'batchelor's buttons', 'Jack-in-the-hedge', 'red Robin', show typical folklore indiscrimination, although together they compile a picture of a weak-stemmed Spring plant, leaning rather than standing against a hedge, with round rosy flowers of button size. 'Campion' (1576), an earlier form of 'champion', is obscure, and here may be one of those words which (like 'derring-do', 'tiffin' or 'pixilated') born of chance or the fancy or error of some particular occasion or person, have become accepted currency. Could its colour have suggested favour worn or trophy won by the champion in the lists? The Latin name is equally far-fetched: '*Melandrium*— name of a plant in Pliny. In Greek cheap cuts of tunny said to resemble chips of black oak'![1] The Sowerby name *dioica lychnis* is more appropriate in that *dioica* indicates that male and female are different plants, but *lychnis* is merely 'the name of a plant in Theophrastus'.

Although red campion grows plentifully in most places, in others it is rare. This may be due to its liking for well-drained acid soils rich in nitrates, which could also explain the extraordinary diversity of its red, sometimes deepest cerise, sometimes palest rose, for it readily hybridises with white campion. Whatever the shade of the petals, so deeply indented as to seem ten instead of five, they are enhanced by their setting in a calyx of dull wine colour. And now you notice that in some plants this dark calyx shelters a large rounded ovary, topped with thread-like stigmas. These are the female flowers, which as in the primrose ripen later than the clusters of stamens borne on other plants, a device for cross-pollination—mainly by humblebees and hoverflies. This spreads their flowering season, as if for our benefit.

[1] H. Gilbert-Carter: *Glossary of the British Flora*.

A beautiful flower, the more so for the company it keeps in hedgebank or woodland, its cool pink, purple-based, consorting well with grey-blue bluebells, greater stitchwort sprinkling its white stars between. But it also seems deliberately to choose a bold clash of colour, the warm greens of unfolding bracken, hartstongue or polypody ferns, and the still more startling yellow-green of wood spurge.

Red Campion with Polypody Fern

WOOD SPURGE
Euphorbia amygdaloides

The memory of a bluebell wood in May is not merely the wellbeloved 'mist of blue': there is often the illumination of a yellow-green colony of wood spurge like sun among shadow, and with red campion added the combination of colour is so daring as to be almost tastable, like William Plomer's birdsong 'sharp as a quince'. The wood spurge itself wears red—the young shoot, crimson as larch cones, pushes up in April from the mop of dark leaves which have survived the winter, to grow a strong red woody stem three feet high, with red on the underside of its leaves, where blue and green are run in as by the brush of a Victorian lady painter. The stance of the whole plant is no less astonishing than its colour—a candelabra of five to eight double-lighted branches curving out from a whorl of bracts, with more branches, each holding two flowers set in a little plate, all down the stem. The flower needs a closer look. The poet Rossetti saw it fortuitously and involuntarily, in one of those moments of acute misery when the mind registers indelibly whatever happens to catch the sight:

> My eyes, wide open, had the run
> Of some ten weeds to fix upon;
> Among those few, out of the sun,
> The woodspurge flowered, three cups in one.
>
> From perfect grief there need not be
> Wisdom or even memory:
> One thing then learnt remains to me—
> The woodspurge has a cup of three.

The 'cup of three' is as complicated a structure as the plant itself, causing one to marvel not for the first time at the intricacy and diversity of pollination devices. Each 'cup' (Gerard's 'saucer' is a more exact picture) holds two little four-petalled flowers on stalks, and one brooch of four tiny golden crescents packed together with their horns facing outwards. Two and one make three.

108

Wood Spurge

Very odd. The interpretation? Each crescent is a nectary, and in the centre where the four meet can be seen (until it ripens and falls off) a pistil—ovary, style and three forked stigmas—surrounded by single anthers, making sexually a complete flower but without sepals or petals, the saucer doing duty for them. The two stalked flowers are actually similar, but are not yet ripe.

If in order to examine the cup of three you have broken off a stem your fingers will be covered with a sticky white juice, which in the New Forest earns the plant the name of Deer's milk. This sap, acrid and poisonous, is common to the Euphorbia family, which yields products as diverse as rubber, castor oil, cassava and tapioca, the last two from manioc root, fortunately rendered harmless by cooking.

It is difficult to see the force of the name 'spurge', for whether it 'drove out' externally (for example, warts of all kinds) or internally as a purge (an old name was 'clensing gras') it could have destroyed more tissue than it cured. Euphorbus, physician to Juba, King of Mauritania, who first discovered its uses, must have had a clear eye and a steady hand to manipulate just the right quantity in exactly the right spot. Gerard has a story, comic in its solemnity, of poisoning by spurge—not our *amygdaloides* ('emerald', descriptive of the vividness though not the shade of its green) but *Euphorbia paralias,* sea spurge:

'Walking along the sea coast at Lee in Essex, with a Gentleman called Mr. Rich, dwelling in the same towne, I tooke but one drop of it into my mouth; which nevertheless did so inflame and swell my throat that I hardly escaped with my life. And in like case was the Gentleman, which caused us to take our horses, and poste for our lives unto the next farme house to drinke some milke to quench the extremitie of our heat, which then ceased.'

HERB PARIS

Paris quadrifolia

I shall not forget my first chance sight of herb paris. Walking in May along a woodland path flanked on either side by overblown bluebells I was suddenly aware of a change in the foliage, for there seems to be some agreement over spheres of influence in the woodland floor. Here it had yielded to herb paris—and among the colony, cradled in the stump of a hazel, was a pheasant's nest with nine eggs.

Herb paris is one of the strangest of plants. At all stages it is conspicuous, first folded up umbrella-wise like a convolvulus, then opening into the crown shape of a wheat rick finial or an unfolding chestnut bud, and at last showing four large green leaves, pair facing pair as they flatten out. Those four leaves would be strange enough alone, and sometimes the plant bears nothing more. But the flower is even more fantastic. Poised at the centre of the cross is a fat spider with shiny black body and green yellow-tipped legs—the round black four-chambered berry, and above it a 'formal geometry' (Massingham's phrase) of four green petals and four slender sepals, the pale gold of the anthers illuminating the eight points of the star.

Perhaps this jewel gave it the name of Lover's knot; other names also point to its use as an aphrodisiac. 'Paris' (Latin *pares,* 'equal') is supposed to relate to the symmetry of its parts, though these are by no means consistent, varying to five and even six leaves. I have found a six-leaved plant with three sepals, three petals, six stamens and a three-part ovary—more appropriate to the order Trilliaceae, to which it belongs: Trillium, which grows wild in North America, is a cousin.

Another name, One-berry, is the same in German. The berry is the most poisonous part of the wholly poisonous plant, which is nevertheless used in small doses by homeopaths. The Doctrine of Signatures might have prompted its use in witchcraft, but was taken the opposite way, and its success as an antidote to black magic and madness was said to be 'affirmed by experience' (Culpeper).

Herb Paris

WOODRUFF

Asperula odorata

When all day long the air is filled with the musical song of the garden warbler and the contented croon of the turtle dove, the ground beneath the edge of the wood is covered with a fine powdering of white, resembling, one imagines, the manna of the Israelites. Woodruff is in bloom. It is called 'Rice flower' where it grows thickly, strewn as for a wedding. So it grows in Germany: it is not so luxuriant here.

Though small the flowers are exquisite, the four milkwhite petals opening out like a dainty cross-stitch with four dark spots at the centre, as whoever first named it 'Lady's needlework' must have seen. Below the flower, in regular tiers round the stem, arise the narrow dark green leaves, eight or nine in a whorl. They are supposed to have given the plant its name of wood 'ruff' or according to Gerard of wood 'rowell' (the wheel of a spur), but the German name Waldmeister, 'wood master' or 'wood reve', suggests an alternative origin. The surname Woodruff may have the same derivation. If not it may be that an interchange of nicknames has taken place: in Germany the woodland plant has been named after the forester, in England it has given its name to the herb-gatherer who collected it.

In the autumn, when the bristly double fruits are ripe, country children used to gather woodruff for herbalists, who made a tisane from its leaves, for they do in fact contain theine. But in all its names, common, local and Latin, is commemorated the faint, sweet, rich scent, coumarin, which is its most charming characteristic—'Sweet woodruff', 'New-mown hay', 'Ladies in the hay', and *Asperula odorata, asperula* ('rough') from the benzoic acid which is the prosaic origin of the perfume.

'Being made into garlands and bundles, hanging up in houses in the heat of summer' says Gerard 'it doth very well attemper the air, coole and make fresh the place to the delight and comfort of such as are therein'. Such garlands sometimes decorated village churches on festival days. The scent grew stronger and still more like hay when the herb was dried; housewives would lay it like lavender in their linen presses, and a cooling drink was

H

113

made from the leaves, sometimes mingled with those of the wild strawberry in wine 'to make the heart merry'. The wine would no doubt do this without the woodruff, but a medicinal excuse was then as now invaluable. With other herbs it made a salve, often appearing in mediaeval recipes as 'Herb Walter', probably after Walter de Elvesden, a writer on medicine. It was even considered potent enough to kill the 'worm' that was thought to have made trouble (ulcer?), besides healing the wound itself: 'Gyf any worme hath y-mad eny hole—Take at the bygynninge and smere the hole with hony and take a poudre of a grace [herb] that men clopyt [call] the woderowe and seethe hit and do hit therto and hit schal sle [slay] the wormys and hele the wonde' (Henslow). Perhaps honey, a proved antiseptic, was the more operative ingredient here.

Woodruff

ASARABACCA

Asarum europaeum

Perhaps asarabacca can hardly be counted as a British wild flower. It is very rare (I know of it in one wood only) and is probably not indigenous, while *Aristolochia* or birthwort, the only other 'British' species in the same order of Aristolochiaceae, if to be found at all is an escape from southern Europe. The medicinal properties of its leaves—purgative, emetic and powdered as snuff—are now more reliably found elsewhere.

Asarabacca is singular in every way. Its outlandish name is a garble of *asara* ('without a wreath') and *baccha* ('berry'), the commonsense if not the meanings of both words lost. Most uncommon too is its strange and beautiful appearance, 'of a very sad or darke grene colour, and shining withal' (Turner). The first unusual thing to be seen, covering a good patch of woodland floor like ivy, is the gleam of its richly glossy leaves. They are rounded into a wide heart shape, or as earlier centuries saw it, a hoof ('Folesfote').

That may well be the last as well as the first one sees of the plant unless one stops to lift the leaves, paler on the underside, and follow the snaking stems to earth level. There, cradled between two stalks, is a curious little brownish thing shaped like a hazelnut still in its husk: the German name for it is Hazelnuss. It always reminds me of the nun Julian of Norwich's report of 'a little thing, the quantity of an hazelnut, in the palm of my hand, and it was as round as a ball . . .' that brought the revelation: 'It lasteth, and ever shall, for that God loveth it.' It is no nut but the three-petalled flower, of a subtle purplish olive to medlar brown, which however Gerard found 'ill favoured'. Hidden though it is, it must contrive to propagate, and once established in a garden the plants appear in fresh places as well as spreading by root.

Asarabacca has foreign cousins, including 'Dutchman's pipe', like *Aristolochia* in form, and Wild Ginger, *Asarum canadensis,* which the first settlers apparently used as a substitute for the ginger they had hoped to find available in North America. To Virginian snakeroot, *Aristolochia serpentaria,* an antidote to snakebite, was also attributed the power of stupefying serpents if placed in their mouths!

116

Asarabacca

BUGLE

Ajuga reptans

Within the damp wood or spreading into its sunnier paths and borders, this 'common' plant even at a glance is strikingly handsome, the spikes of blue flowers rising erect from their encircling mats of purple-brown runners. No wonder the more showy *pyramidalis* variety is grown in gardens.

Bugle deserves close and careful scrutiny. That spire, thickening rather than tapering as it rises, seems from May to July to be perpetually in bloom, because at any one time only a third of its flowers are out. How elaborately and cunningly they are arranged! a dozen tiers of whorls ('rundles' Gerard calls them) all the way up the stem. Seen from directly above, the opposite pairs of leaves with the four open flowers in their axils make ornate crosses one below the other. Twelve flowers, all but those four still in bud, go to a circle, six a side with a space between.

Did this ornamentation suggest the old name bugle (bead)? Or was it the rich and varied colour of the whole plant? the leaves copper-veined, copper at the edges and bright violet, especially on the satin underside where they join the empurpled stem; the labiate flowers in their pointed wine-dyed calyxes a variety of blues—pale and pearly at the base, beautifully marked with deeper violet on wing petals and lower lip, the bright yellow anthers under the little cleft upper lip in sharp contrast.

More likely 'bugle' is an unromantic corruption of *Ajuga*, itself a corruption of *Abiga*, vaguely glossed as 'driver-away', perhaps of the foetus, but more probably of sores. Its name 'Middle comfrey'—comfrey the long-established knitter of wounds and even of bones—perpetuates its healing powers, whether as medicine or as a salve, while 'Sickle-wort' and 'Carpenter's herb' are reminders that even a skilled workman sometimes cuts himself.

A white variety, without the copper and violet tinges, is sometimes found. Sir John Salusbury, 1567-1612, (son of the William Salusbury who first translated the New Testament into Welsh) records with invaluable exactness of place and time the plants he found in Wales: 'Bugle or Middle

Comfrey also White flowered Bugle: I Sir John Salusbury, Knight, found both in Lleweny park in the coppice adjoining upon the River Cloyd where the herbes Adders tonge and Twiblade growe. I found them the XXth of May 1606 growing there plentifullie.'

Bugle

COMMON SOLOMON'S SEAL
Polygonatum multiflorum
and
ANGULAR SOLOMON'S SEAL
Polygonatum odoratum

We all know Solomon's seal as a garden flower of May, its long stem weighed down in a sweeping arc by the clusters of long creamy-white bells, green within and greenish at tip and base, the leaves all along the stalk 'standing poised above the hanging bells with a grace as of wings'.[1]

It is however a wild flower though local, an early import into gardens for its many purposes. It grows vigorously in the shade of a hillside wood in limestone country, its presence first betrayed by snakes' heads 'with an eye of bluish upon the green' (Culpeper), long close-furled oval shapes tensed to strike at the tips of their stems. At this stage the young shoots—like those of too many other plants!—have been eaten as asparagus.

Why Solomon's seal? It is the name used in all the herbals, and in French, German, Italian and Spanish. The 'seal' is said to refer to the scars left by the stems along the rootstock, but except that they could be stamped-out marks they bear little resemblance to a seal, still less to Solomon's seal which, since he was a popular figure in the Middle Ages, was the Arab name for the Star of David. He presumably came into it because of his reputed knowledge of (among other things) the magical properties of plants, his seal, metaphorical rather than literal, setting a guarantee of their efficacy. There is besides the physical sense of 'seal' as healer of broken surfaces, for which the roots of this plant were chiefly used; it may be the 'knyttewort' of early recipes.

Gerard, facetious as Culpeper for once, says that an application 'taketh away in one night, or two at the most, any bruise, blacke or blew spots

[1] Massingham: *Shepherd's Country*.

120

Common Solomon's Seal

gotten by fals, or womens wilfulnesse in stumbling upon their hasty husbands fists or such like'. It was not only a healer but a cosmetic, 'leaving the place fresh, fair and lovely, for which purpose it is much used by the Italian dames' Culpeper tells us. 'Following only Dr. Experience' he found there was 'not a better medicine under the Sun . . . stamped and boiled in wine it speedily helps (being drunk I mean, for it will not do the deed by looking upon it) all broken bones'. A mediaeval writer warns that the patient should be kept from 'contrarious metes and drynkes tille he be hot, and lete hym alaway bere a balle of herbes or sumwhat elys in hys hond'.

There are two other wild varieties of Solomon's seal. One, of very different habit, is *Polygonatum verticillatum,* Whorled Solomon's seal, very rare and found only in Scotland and Northumberland. The other, *Polygonatum odoratum,* Angular Solomon's seal, though also rare can be found growing along with *Polygonatum multiflorum,* which may be why they have hybridised in gardens. It is a smaller plant, with fewer though larger flowers than those of *multiflorum,* as this name indicates: from the base of each leaf, four or five to a plant, dangles a single bell, or occasionally two, whereas *multiflorum* has five, six, seven or eight clusters of two, three or four flowers. This means that the stance and display of *multiflorum* is much the more beautiful. The term 'angular' is not really distinctive enough, for the generic *polygonatum* means 'many-angled', and the stem's change of direction between leaf and leaf, marked in the angular variety, is just noticeable in *multiflorum* too. *Odoratum* is an alternative description recording the faint almond perfume which *multiflorum* lacks.

It seems strange that it was this rarer scented variety which was called *officinale,* that is, included in the official pharmaceutical register; still stranger therefore that Mrs. Grieve should say of it feebly: 'The properties of these roots have not been very fully investigated. *Polygonatum officinale* is said to be no longer used.'

Angular Solomon's Seal

YELLOW PIMPERNEL (WOOD LOOSESTRIFE)

Lysimachia nemorum

It was Lysimachos, King of Sicily, who, they say, in first discovering its uses gave its name to this little herb, which could assuage fever, soothe sore eyes or teeth, staunch blood. But the vernacular has a way of finding for strange words a meaning within its experience: surely the plant had not been called 'loosestrife' (the literal translation of Greek *Lysimachia*—for all personal names have their meanings) without good reason, and therefore it might appease 'the strife and unrulinesse which falleth out among oxen at the plough, if it be put about their yokes'—as a fly-repellent?

It is no relation whatever to purple loosestrife, which became confused with another tall riverbank plant, yellow loosestrife, *Lysimachia vulgaris;* but its small size and neat pattern show it as kin to the pimpernels, scarlet and blue, which like the Lysimachias are members of the primrose family.

At first you may easily mistake it for Creeping Jenny, *Lysimachia nummularia,* but the likeness is superficial. The five-pointed stars of yellow pimpernel, that hang one to the right one to the left on the slenderest threads of stems, are smaller than Creeping Jenny's and crisp and perfect in form. Lying on the moss below are yet more stars, for when the flower is over the corolla drops entire, still shapely and unfaded. So symmetrical are the petals that the calyx showing in the spaces between them forms another star, narrow and green, behind the golden one, and at the centre the purple anthers curl over in a little fountain. The light green leaves are not circular like Creeping Jenny's but finely shaped ovals, glossy beneath like those of celandine and moschatel and sanicle, that also love moist places.

Though once rare enough to be recorded as growing 'in the woods between Highgate and Hampstead', the flower today will sometimes cover whole acres of the woodland that gives its name *nemorum*.

Yellow Pimpernel

WOOD FORGET-ME-NOT
Myosotis sylvatica

There are many kinds of wild forget-me-not, varied in habitat from riverside to mountain, in the depth of their blue from near-grey to full turquoise and in the colour of bud from white and cream to pink and even yellow, in size of flower from minute to significant, in height from dwarf and creeping to tall. All have the downy or hairy leaves of the borage family: *myosotis* refers to their mouse-ear texture.

The wood forget-me-not, with water forget-me-not, is the largest, with the largest leaves, and of all it is the tallest, most distinguished in its proud erect stance among the young bracken still curled like the heads of cellos. It too curves over at the top, as do all forget-me-nots in that classic one-sided flowering 'cyme': their name 'scorpion grass' comes from the curl of the scorpion's tail in its aggressive pose. But the Wood is not the brightest of the forget-me-nots: the blue is soft and pale, yet not faded but conspicuous in the shade of the wood.

The forget-me-not flower is exquisite in design as in colour. The five light skyblue petals, mostly round, sometimes slightly pointed, meet at the centre in a raised star, golden, cream or white, and between its points are five longer points, white streaks down the centres of the petals. No wonder it is seen so often in embroidery, in painting, in china with pansies and roses; no wonder it breathes romance and the language of flowers.

'Forget-me-not' now seems the inevitable name, not only to us but to France and Germany ('Ne m'oubliez pas', 'Vergiss-mein-nicht') if not to more European countries. But although some foreign forms denote an earlier origin, it was not current in Britain till the nineteenth century, and seems to have been introduced from Germany, where arose the rather absurd story of the gallant lover carried away by the stream as he bent to pick the flower for his sweetheart, throwing it to her with his farewell cry. The story, one suspects, was invented to fit the flower.

126

Wood Forget-me-not

SANICLE

Sanicula europaea

The name gives some idea, though not enough, of how widespread is this plant: it is found in every part of the British Isles except Orkney and Shetland, but it grows also in Siberia, Persia, India, Malaya, Madagascar, China and Japan. This wide distribution may be due in part to its method of seed dispersal—by burs which like those of goosegrass cling to any moving thing they touch.

In other European languages also it is known as sanicle, a proof of the healing powers which lay in the whole plant, mainly for internal leakages and breakages but also for external wounds. Henslow has twelve recipes for salves containing the herb 'wodemerche' (wood boundary) glossed as 'sanicle'. The French proverbs are no doubt echoed in other tongues:

> Celui qui Sanicle a
> De mire affaire il n'a

and

> Qui a la Sanicle
> Fait aux chirugiens la niche.

('He who has sanicle has nothing better', and 'Who has sanicle can cock a snook at the surgeons.')

It would be interesting to know whether its use spread directly and indirectly from the writings of the earliest physicians or whether it arose spontaneously among primitive peoples by trial and error, for neither by doctrine of signatures nor by any other spectacular quality would it attract notice: it must be the least showy of our Umbelliferae.

Yet what a beautiful plant it is! Individually the flowers are minute and the umbels sparse and irregular, but their charming little 'mossie' balls (Gerard's word) make a full display of their haloes of ripe stamens, pink and creamy white like the petals. Only a few flowers in the centre also have pistils, which however make the most of their chance by protruding even beyond the bud. Others compensate for their sterility by having larger and more conspicuous

128

Sanicle

petals. The leaves, that in early May scatter their little patterns all over the wood, when full-grown have the classical form of vine or maple; they are richly dark, but with a contrasting pale underside, glossy as fine porcelain. Moreover sanicle, flowering when the glory of May is over, is seen to full advantage as a most individual and unusual flower, and an assurance that the woodland still has surprises in store.

CUCKOO-PINT

Arum maculatum

So startling, so outlandish is this plant that it is not surprising that it should be (with *Arum neglectum*) the only British species of its order, Araceae. Even the lovely white arum lily looks more native to our greenhouses than this kindred plant to our woods, the dark spike wrapped in its pale green purple-spotted sheath rising from arrow-shaped purple-spotted leaves.

Its very oddness has made it familiar to the most botanically ignorant countryman, who has surely given it more names than any other wild flower. Some, like Parson-in-the-pulpit and Friar's cowl, refer to its enveloping hood or 'spathe'; many, like Snake's-food, to its poisonous properties; as many to the two kinds of 'spadix' (the 'parson', dark or pale)—Lords and Ladies, Kings and Queens; and many are the 'grosser names'—Cuckoo-pint (penis), Dog cocks. For these are poor Ophelia's 'long purples' (a Warwickshire name), less likely certainly to be found by a brookside than tall purple loosestrife, but more 'fantastic', and alas, more in keeping with the fixation that comes out in her mad snatches of song.

> There with fantastic garlands did she come
> Of crowflowers, nettles, daisies, and long purples,
> That liberal shepherds give a grosser name.
> But our cold maids do dead-men's-fingers call them.

'Dead men's fingers' is the exact description of the ghastly mauve-greys and inky greens of some of the 'long purples'. The variety in cuckoo-pint is remarkable. In some the spathe is dyed deepest purple, while others are tinged at the edges only and yet others not at all; some are unspotted or scarcely spotted, others bespattered, yet others heavily blotched—*maculatum* (spotted) is indeed well earned. Some spathes are widespread, but as many are slender and elongated, while the dye may be wine-red, brownish, greenish, or nearly black.

The sole purpose of the spectacular spadix is to attract small insects, which enter the lower close-wrapped part holding stamens and pistils and stay

131

there, held by a ring of hairs, long enough to cross-pollinate on emerging when the hairs wither. A 'lady' spadix, pale against the pale sheath, seems much less usefully conspicuous here than a 'lord', and reminds one of the handsome *Arum italicum,* wild in southern France, with creamy yellow spadix and beautifully cream-veined leaves, a single plant of which flowers among the 'mille fleurs' of the Unicorn tapestry. Pheasants wintering in our garden perversely prefer it to the native arum, at the same time digging with disastrous abandon for the tuberous roots of both kinds, which strangely enough after much processing can yield an edible sort of tapioca and of arrowroot. They also eat with impunity even the poisonous bright scarlet berries left clustering on their naked stems at the end of summer.

Cuckoo-pint and Common Cow-wheat

COMMON COW-WHEAT

Melampyrum pratense

Although cow-wheat is called *pratense* ('meadow'), in this country it is rather an inhabitant of woods, where it is partially parasitic on roots. Gerard says it grows 'upon Hampsted Heath neere London, among the juniper bushes and bilberry bushes in all parts of the said heath, and in every part of England where I have travelled'. It is now rather rare anywhere.

Melampyrum means 'black wheat', descriptive of the seeds, which when ground with grain were supposed to make the bread dark. This, like its German name Wachtelweizen (quail wheat) must apply to *Melampyrum arvense,* the field variety, perhaps the one Linnaeus means when he says 'The best and yellowest butter is made where this plant abounds'. But even *Melampyrum pratense* prefers the edges of woods rather than the centre, among the bracken that betrays a lime-free soil.

Pale-flowered, dark and narrow of leaf, and of low growth, spindly and branching, cow-wheat can easily pass unnoticed, but seen closely is an unusual and beautiful plant, as are many of the less-known of the Scrophularia family. The creamy-white hood of the corolla seems to be nearly out of its calyx, yet of all insects only the bee is strong enough to push between the two lower lips, of a velvety calceolaria gold. The yellowish green buds are tipped and the calyx is spotted with wine colour, revealing the relationship to the spectacular crested bartsia of French roadsides, astonishing in its combination of gold and orange flowers with showy magenta calyxes.

Cow-wheat has no more than five or six flowers out at a time, but like those of the kindred red bartsia of our roadsides they all face in the same direction, and it is this habit of growth, together with the arrangement in alternate pairs of its leaves, deeply toothed like the calyxes of crested bartsia, that betrays its presence.

LILY-OF-THE-VALLEY
Convallaria majalis

'It groweth on Hampsted heath in great abundance' says Gerard. Hampstead Heath, which till the end of the eighteenth century was wooded, must have been a floral paradise. But no flower so pure, so lovely and with so delicious a scent, 'comfortable for the memory and senses' (Turner), could hope to escape depredation. Moreover it was used by herbalists as a milder substitute for digitalis, despite being, according to the HMSO publication *Poisonous Plants* (1954), poisonous in every part, especially the flowers. 'Geese and fowls have been killed through eating the leaves' it warns, too late for Mrs. Grieve. 'A good price is obtainable for the flowers' she writes in 1931, 'and in Lincolnshire, Derbyshire, Westmorland and other counties, where the plant grows freely wild, they would pay for collecting'. And to extract the perfume a dozen infusions are needed, each time of fresh flowers! The plant of course intends the perfume for the bee, which is rewarded for its visits not with nectar but with pollen. The French name 'muguet' is derived from the root of 'musk', apparently applied in a plant to scent of any kind. Turner's recipe, presumably for perfume, sounds like an old wives' tale: 'Having filled a glasse with the flowers, and being well stopped, set it for a months space in an Antshill, and after being drayned cleare, set it by to use'. The 'Leechdoms' had a less extravagant and also more practical use for the plant as a salve, more lard than lily (the plant was then thought to have been given to Aesculapius by Apollo): 'Against sore hands, take the same wort Apollinaris, knock it with old lard without salt, do thereto a cup of old wine and let it be hot without smoke, and of the lard let there be a pound's weight, knock together in the way thou mightest work a plaster and lay it to the hands' (Cockayne).

Partly because so many woods have been destroyed, and also because people near lily-of-the-valley woods 'know for' them, pick and uproot them for their gardens, and sometimes even sell them in the nearest towns, they could hardly be said to grow 'freely' today unless in carefully guarded secrecy. Yet where they are well established in the moist limestone woods

135

they prefer—the slopes rather than the valleys—their strong creeping roots will grow through stone walls. Though they like the shade they will advance into the open, even to the bridleway, surviving in the very cart tracks. The earliest sign of their presence in a wood is a sudden area of fresh green V's, double-tongued green flames all over the ground; still earlier the V has been a tightly rolled spill. Now it is unfurling to reveal the two leaves that enfold the flower, though you will not find a flower in every pair. The fragile yet wiry curving stem is hung with six or seven small creamy yellow pearls, which gradually open, lowest first, into purest white rounded bells, upcurled at the tips 'like little hollow bottles with open mouths' (Turner). By this time, grown larger, the leaves have taken on a beautiful grape-like bloom.

'May lily' and 'May bells' one often hears, but perhaps the prettiest, most evocative names are the Dorset 'Innocents' and 'Lily constancy' or 'Liriconfancie', which are merely corruptions of the Latin. So romantic a flower, redolent of Victorian valentines, deserves to bloom at the peak of the year, when primrose and anemone if past their prime look yet more luxuriant in full leaf or in fruit, later comers like columbine are already in bud, and all the May flowers it seems are out together. Oak and sycamore are in catkin and coppery leaf, chestnut already bearing white cones, and the beech 'flaps its glad green leaves like wings, delicate filmed as new-spun silk'. Gardens are tipsy with apple blossom, lilac and laburnum, tulips, forget-me-nots and wallflowers. All the migrants are here—chiffchaff, willow wren, blackcap, nightingale, garden warbler, turtledove, while 'the cuckoo sends afloat his note on the air all day'. If only spring could last forever!

Lily-of-the-valley

WHITE HELLEBORINE

Cephalanthera damasonium

White helleborine is not a common orchid, partly because of its very marked preference for limestone beechwoods in southern England, and for mossy and stony situations in these. There, since so little grows well under beech trees, it is easily seen, but because of its stance, with pale green leaves ascending the twisted stem, rather than for its flowers, which since they never seem to open properly scarcely suggest orchid at all, looking more like creamy waxen buds, tulip shaped.

Indeed something may have gone wrong with the plant, for it is self-fertilised, and self-fertilisation tends to perpetuate defects: having no need to attract insects its petals remain half closed. Yet the very restriction of its orifice makes those insects—notably bees—which visit it brush more closely first against the sticky stigma and then against the stamens curled under the hood. They are offered a guide at the entrance in the tempting yellow-furred ribs on the lower petal. These, said Darwin (who must have sampled them) taste of vanilla, and small mouthfuls are seen to have been nibbled off! Evolutionarily it seems as though the plant instead of displaying its petals has developed underground buds as an additional means of reproduction.

For creamy white ovals with a core of yellow, 'egg orchid' is an apt name. Not so Pliny's name *cephalanthera*, for the anthers, as is common, are at the throat of the flower, not at the head, *cephale*. *Damasonium* (of Damascus) would confirm that the plant grows as far east as Asia Minor. But why, for anything so totally unlike hellebores, 'helleborine'?

There is another much rarer white helleborine, the narrow-leaved or sword-leaved, *Cephalanthera longifolia,* which so far I have found only in Provence. Its leaves are longer and narrower, thrusting sharply and strikingly upwards, and its flowers are smaller and whiter.

White Helleborine

GREATER BUTTERFLY ORCHID
Platanthera chlorantha

The time to hunt for the butterfly orchid is a late evening at the end of May or in early June, just when the nightingale is beginning to tune up at the fringe of the wood. Then, if you do not at first see the spike of flowers, ghostly in the gathering dusk, you may catch the 'Night violet's' sweet, exotic, feminine fragrance, that vanishes entirely with sunrise.

If you are looking for something like a butterfly—or like any insect, unless perhaps a small dragonfly—you will search in vain. The Bristol name 'white angel orchid' gives a far better idea of the creamy or greenish white flowers (*chlorantha*) poised a dozen or a score or so about the tall stem that rises more than a foot from its twayblade-like root leaves. The angel's head is the upper petal, the spread wings the side ones, the body the long lower lip that has earned it the name *habenaria*—'thong-like', and if your fancy likes to go so far, a wisp of robe or of hair—the extraordinary long spur—trails behind. Each angel is arrested in flight, as it were, by the violent twist of stalk typical of orchids, designed so to arrange the flowers that they may be easily reached by the visiting night moths which the scent attracts. (*Platanthera* refers to this arrangement.) Guarding the entrance to the spur are the two stamens whose pollen the moths carry away with them, and in return, when they thrust their long tongues through the opening circular as a woodworm's hole, they are rewarded by nectar so plentiful that it moves up the spur visibly when it is pinched.

To find one butterfly orchid, perhaps in a hazel copse, is to find two, three; then four, five, six or more, but the growth is too sparse to deserve the word 'colony'. They are not common. But where the soil is limestone and kindly they are not likely to vanish unless picked, and they grow tall and strong, so that some botanists wonder whether the greater and the lesser varieties may not be merely finer and poorer specimens of the selfsame plant.

Even in Gerard's day when, like lilies-of-the-valley, they grew as near London as Hampstead Heath, they were rare enough to warrant an exact

Greater Butterfly Orchid

description of the sites. 'That kind which resembleth the white Butter-fly groweth upon the declining of the hill at the end of Hampsted heath, neere to a small cottage there in the way side, as yee goe from London to Henden a village there by. It groweth in the fields adjoining to the fold or pin-fold without the gate, at a village called High-gate neere London: and likewise in the wood belonging to a Worshipfull gentleman of Kent named Mr. Sidley, of Southfleet: where doe grow likewise many other rare and dainty simples, that are not to be found elsewhere in great circuit.

'There is no great use of these in physicke, but they are chiefly regarded for the pleasant and beautiful flours wherewith Nature hath seemed to play and disport her selfe.'

FLY ORCHID

Ophrys insectifera

A plant that resorts to mimicry to gain its ends must surely be nearly human. To attract pollinating insects this orchid sets out to be a fly—wings, antennae, colour (dark brown-purple with a bluish patch), body 'with a shew of legs hanging at it' and all, even to the poise, set rakishly on the stem. 'The natural Flie' continues Turner 'seemeth so to be in love with it, that you shall seldome come in the heat of the day but you shall finde one sitting close thereon.'

Where it fails in its purpose the plant produces no seeds of its own, thus having barely enough to keep up its numbers. Even then it will grow only on chalk or limestone, sometimes rashly near or even in the trodden path.

142

Fly Orchid

BIRD'S-NEST ORCHID

Neottia nidus-avis

This is one of the oddest of the odd family of orchids: in some years scarce, in others plentiful; anything from six to twenty inches high; leafless; and brown all over all the year round, except for (if one looks closely enough) pale yellow anthers clustering round a purplish stigma. Dispensing with chlorophyll, the plant is a saprophyte, getting its nourishment through its 'bird's nest', a tangled mop of roots infected with the useful fungus which enables it to feed on the decaying mulch of the woodland floor. Its botanical name is redundant—'bird's nest' twice over, first in Greek and then in Latin.

Though not in colour bird's-nest orchid is striking in form. In late May or early June you may find rising from dead leaves and beech mast what looks like an opening head of darkened maize, or a packet of tightly crammed brown beads—the flower buds furled in a brown sheath. When the orchid has grown to its full height you can count the beads, grown into brown flowers with a cleft lower lip, anything from twenty-five to forty-five set round the stout ribbed six-sided stem like a bottle-brush.

But it is strangest and most conspicuous when mummified in the depths of winter and the depths of the lifeless wood. The tall dry stem still keeps its characteristic orchidal twist. The fruits, hardened poppy-heads, might be ancient nutmegs from some Egyptian tomb. At a still later stage they no longer rattle, having split to shed their seeds, but only at top and bottom, the six ribs still holding, so that they look like little lantern-towers, or Chinese balls carved in wood instead of ivory. In death as in life they are marvels, scarcely of the plant world.

Buds of Bird's-nest Orchid

Flower & fruit of Bird's-nest Orchid

BASTARD BALM

Melittis melissophyllum

Bastard balm is a rare plant of damp woodland, hedge or bank, rare enough to be included in the *Red Data Book*, the conservationist survey; but where it does grow, chiefly in Cornwall and South Devon, it may be found in quantity. To be fortunate enough to come upon it unawares must be the experience of a lifetime.

'Bastard' sounds a derogatory name (like cow-parsley or dog-rose) for such a handsome plant, the largest of our labiates: *grandiflora* or *spectabilis* or *pulchrissima* would suit it better. Only two of the whorled flowers, front-facing, are in bloom at a time. The colour varies, but resolves into two kinds. In one the lower lip is stained reddish purple, with a white margin; the other's is white with deep pink or magenta spots or streaks. If you look at the flower sideways the force of its Latin honey names is at once clear: the calyx seems far too loose for the long nectar-filled corolla tube. From the front it calls to mind a little Edwardian girl dressed in a pretty wide-sleeved frock and floppy hat, or one of those small flat cardboard dolls of the same period supplied with a set of gay dresses to be hitched on with little tabs at the shoulder.

The plant is not of course a true 'balsam' (whose ultimate meaning is 'scent'), and 'bastard' probably indicates that is has neither the perfume nor the healing properties of the lemon balm, *Melittis officinalis,* of old-fashioned gardens, a salad herb which yields good wine and refreshing tisane. However, had it ever been common enough, bastard balm's herbal smell, akin to that of woundwort or ground ivy, might have led to its use in medicine. 'Why bastard? wherefore base?' In this case a reminder that the illegitimate often turns out to be not the black sheep or ugly duckling of the family but its star.

Bastard Balm and Cuckoo-pint

WOOD VETCH

Vicia sylvatica

Papilionaceae is a handsome family, the family of the fodder crops, the clovers, peas and vetches, yellow, white, pink, red, blue or purple, the pretty shape of the flower often accentuated by differentiation of the colours of its parts—standard, wings and keel—as in the everlasting pea tamed in our gardens. Of our wild vetches the most beautiful as well as the most spectacular is the wood vetch. It is also unfortunately the most rare, or rather perhaps it is local, according to the flora[1] 'in rocky bushy places, woods and shingle and cliffs by the sea' and to Sowerby 'hitherto supposed peculiar to the mountainous parts of England and Wales'. Anne Pratt quotes Scott, not normally so observant a botanist and so all the more familiar with the plant:

> Where profuse the wood vetch clings
> Round ash and elm in slender rings.
> Its pale and azure-pencilled flower
> Should canopy Titania's bower.

I have seen it only once—and then had to be led there—in one of the two localities mentioned by John Goodyer (b.1592), a Wiltshire wood, by no means mountainous, rocky, shingly or near the sea, though necessarily 'bushy'. Cascading over brambles and briers in a clearing it made a magnificent display, the crowded crocketed spires of large palest grey flowers, delicately veined in blue with a purple blotch at the lower lip, rising from the horizontal stems. As striking as the flowers were the leaves, symmetrically designed in oval pairs all the way up the stalk ending in those gracefully curling yet powerful tendrils that haul the plant along and aloft. And all this in July, when trees have assumed a uniform green, and the woodland seems to have comparatively little to compensate for the lost glories of spring.

---

[1] Clapham, Tutin and Warburg.

K*

Wood Vetch

MONKSHOOD

Aconitum anglicum

Monkshood is a familiar garden plant, but few in this country can have seen it growing wild unless while travelling in the Alps. I have found it only twice, and that with foreknowledge of its whereabouts—once in a wet wood, once by a stream, on either side of the Bristol Channel and almost equidistant from it, both places luckily almost inaccessible unless to a determined seeker. Its dark purplish blue, nearly indigo, would scarcely be seen in the darkness of a wood if it did not grow in tall spires, and in a colony.

It is a strange, arresting flower, helmeted rather than hooded, reminding me of Rembrandt's painting of a young knight. The buds at the top of the tall stem are folded up like foetuses, but when the vizor of the helmet is lifted the fully open flower looks stranger still, a grinning face displaying whiskers, a forked beard, and a bunch of 'teeth' (the stamens) in the open mouth.

It is no surprise to learn that it is the most poisonous of all our plants: 'aconite' may be derived from the word for 'spear', referring to its use for poisoning arrows. What is surprising is that more people are poisoned by it than by any other plant, for neither its dark dye nor its acrid smell tempts the palate. *Anglicum* testifies to its long use as a drug in this country, where it is a native. Before the considerable variation in the strength of its poisonous alkaloid was known it may have been administered indiscriminately—and maybe not always accidentally! Parkinson warns his readers: 'although their beauty may be entertained . . . yet beware they come not neare your tongue or lippes, lest they tell you to your cost, they are not so good as they seem to be'.

Legends of it abound: it was concocted by Hecate from the foam of the dog Cerberus, guardian of Hell; it was used by Circe in her enchantments; its roots were devoured by Mark Antony's starving soldiers, who died in convulsions and hallucinations; it was the substance that made witches fly. Parkinson recommends a 'counterpoison' variety, apparently the equally deadly yellow mountain monkshood, 'not onely against the poison of the poisonfull Helmet flower, and all others of that kinde, but also against the

151

poison of all venemous beasts, the plague or pestilence, and other infectious diseases, which raise spots, pockes or markes in the outward skinne, by expelling the poison from within, and defending the heart as a most soveraigne cordiall'. Was it the primitive and dangerous identification of light (yellow) and dark (indigo) with good and evil?

Notwithstanding, like deadly nightshade, *Aconitum anglicum* yields a useful drug, both as liniment and as anodyne, another example of 'medicine in large quantities is the worst poison: poison in minute quantities is the best medicine'.

Monkshood

COMMON WINTERGREEN
Pyrola minor

'Common' and 'lesser' wintergreen are misnomers, and mean only that this *Pyrola* is less rare than the other British varieties—*rotundifolia, media, uniflora* and *secunda*. The two last must once have been familiar enough in the north to acquire local names, the single-flowered 'St. Olaf's candlestick' and 'Yeavering bells' with flowers hanging all down one side of the stem in a row. This name is a pun on Yeavering Bell, a hill in the Cheviots bearing the old name 'bell' for 'beacon'. The North American name is 'side bells'. *Pyrola minor* is very local, preferring the north as do all wintergreens, and likes an open glade or pathside in pinewoods. I have seen it growing sparsely in a beechwood in the west of England, but in quantity only in the Savoy Alps, overspreading mossy mounded tree-roots.

At first sight the rounded creamy bells could easily be mistaken for lily-of-the-valley not yet fully opened, but there the resemblance ends: they are spherical rather than bell-shaped, revealing kinship with arbutus, pieris, heather, and the natural order ericaceae. Moreover the time of flowering is late summer, July to August. The leaves may be called pear-shaped (*pyrola*), but as they are by no means pear-sized the name is hardly helpful. Pyrola creeps and spreads in a colony; that and the way the erect, almost wiry-looking stems rise in small spikes of flowers from their rosettes remind one of bugle.

Such a dainty, rare little plant does not look as though it would yield quantities of the aromatic unguent that facilitates the massage—if it does not itself ease the pain—of rheumaticky joints. Nor is this the plant: the salve which contains among other things resin and silicic acid comes from a North American *Pyrola,* Pipsissewa (*Chimaphila umbellata*), evergreen and creeping like our own, but much more widespread. There it is called rheumatism weed as well as wintergreen, and is used internally also, especially for kidney and skin diseases, as is our *Pyrola minor*—or was, if or when it really was 'common'.

154

Common Wintergreen

CREEPING JENNY
Lysimachia nummularia

Creeping Jenny's many names—Wandering sailor, Meadow runagates, Herb twopence, String of sovereigns—tell us almost all we need to know to identify it and distinguish it easily from *Lysimachia nemorum,* (wood loosestrife or yellow pimpernel, q.v.).

It loves damp woods and streamsides—Gerard found it on the banks of the Thames 'right against the Queenes palace of White-hall'—but also likes sun, advancing towards the open by its creeping overground stems (like strawberry runners) so swiftly and surely that it seems to have abandoned the idea of setting seed. To give its round leaves maximum light and breathing space it arranges them face upwards in pairs on either side of the stem like a double row of coins. They are yellowish green; the flowers, five-petalled but by no means starry like yellow pimpernel's, are a rather dull flat yellow of the same tone as the leaves, so that the charm of the plant lies much less in colour and shape of flower than in the all-over pattern it weaves over the ground throughout June and July, every space in every direction filled with leaflet or flower.

For an attempt to explain 'Lysimachia' see yellow pimpernel. Maybe because of its creeping progress, folklore associated *Lysimachia nummularia* with snakes, which when wounded were said to cure themselves with it! Did they 'know' of its anti-haemorrhage powers? Herbalists anyway have done, from times past to the present day.

Creeping Jenny

COLUMBINE

Aquilegia vulgaris

Most people would hardly think of the columbine as a wild flower nowadays. It is said to be native in Devonshire, but is also called a garden escape. I know of three limestone woods which had a small colony each, but two of these were privately preserved and the third has been ruthlessly ploughed. Yet any plant with seed so abundant, capable of lying dormant for over twenty years, should have survived, especially as it is not used in medicine. It may never have been common, *vulgaris* merely distinguishing it from the more sophisticated varieties. Keen seventeenth-century gardeners may well have transferred wild plants, without any sense of depredation, to their elaborately laid-out plots, an 'escape' in the opposite direction.

The wild columbine is a dark violet blue, and one of its many charms is the beautiful interchange of purple and glaucous green on leaf, stem and bud. It is handsome for its leaves alone, increasingly complex as they descend the stem, the three-lobed leaves that rise from the root prettily crenellated, with the suggestion of the shape of a giant maidenhair fern. Then early in June comes the flower, a five-fold cluster of little doves meeting head-on, suspended from a gracefully down-curved stem.

Hence the name, from the Latin *columba*, 'dove', and the early name culverwort, from Anglo-Saxon *culfre*, 'woodpigeon'—dove certainly, the 'affronting' doves at drinking bowls in Italian mosaics, rather than eagle (*aquila*), which could only apply to the talon-like curve of the spurs, 'little hollowe hornes' as Gerard calls them. One wonders which insects reach the bottom of these spurs (the doves' 'necks') for their nectar. It is not surprising to learn that the American wild columbine is visited by hummingbirds. The many granny-bonnet names describe the double frilly columbines, both pinks and purples, of our gardens, while the scarlet flower with yellow centre, *Aquilegia canadensis,* is too late an introduction to earn a nickname at all. Children should have found one for the miniature peapods that can be shelled and made to scatter their hundreds of thousands of grains. What happens to them all?

158

Columbine

If the columbine is but rarely found in the woods, its decorative pictorial quality has won it pride of place in the world of art. Dürer's loving watercolour of 'Wald Akerlei' at once comes to mind, with the columbines, roses and pansies bordering manuscripts, and the myriad shapes of bell, cross, star and heart woven into tapestries in the fifteenth century. Here the columbine had also its significance in the elaborate convention of chivalry echoed in its romantic Italian name, Perfetto Amore.

BETONY
Stachys officinalis

Since betony is happy in woods it may justifiably be included here, for it asks to be drawn, as much for the beautiful symmetrical scallops of its leaf edges as for its poised tiers of rich red flowers, their anthers spotted bright brown and cream, separated by bare stalk—an 'interrupted spike' in botanical terms, among labiates peculiar to betony. Spike, or ear of corn, is the meaning of the Greek *stachys*. However, I myself have more often found betony outside a wood than deep within it:

> a sentry of dark betonies,
> The stateliest of small flowers on earth,
> At the forest verge.[1]

It was certainly to the fields, no doubt once woodland, that our neighbouring herb-gatherers used to repair forty years ago, pulling up the plant root and all, alas, according to instructions, to dry spread out on the roofs of their cottage garden sheds and privies.

As the name *officinalis* implies, its medicinal uses were proven and manifold, renowned through the centuries from the time of the Emperor Augustus's physician, who wrote a whole treatise on it, to the present day with its herbal teas and nerve tonics. 'Betony' is supposedly derived from 'Vettones', a Spanish tribe who discovered it, and the old saying 'as many virtues as betony' is Spanish. An indication of its antiquity is the injunction in Anglo-Saxon 'Leechdoms' that it must be gathered 'in August month, without iron', a superstition linked with far-off pagan legends of Wayland's smithy and Sigurd's sword. Among the powers it was supposed to possess were (as usual) purging, promoting sneezing, healing wounds, staunching bleeding and breaking stone. It was also a cure for dropsy, sciatica, jaundice, coughs, earache, toothache, headache, stomach-ache, hysteria (with mistletoe, millipedes etc.), cataract ('the pyn in a mannes eye'), the falling sickness, against monstrous nightgoers and against fearful sights and

[1] Edward Thomas: 'The sun used to shine.'

L

161

dreams. Finally it was the panacea 'for alle seknesse in mannys body, and for al the membrys of mannys body: [lay] an addre amydde the sercle the addre schal nought come at hym; if thou ete bytayne fastyng thou schal nought be a-veneryd [lustful] that day, thou schalt nogt be dronke that day, thou schalt have nought ye palsy' (Henslow).

Betony

ENCHANTER'S NIGHTSHADE
Circaea lutetiana

How did this plant come by 'this charmingly romantic term for an unattractive and tiresome garden weed'?[1] It bears no resemblance to any nightshade, and belongs, unlikely as it may seem, to the same family as willow-herb and evening primrose. It is a puzzle how so insignificant and harmless a plant, never used as medicine, should have been sufficiently noted to be confused with anything, let alone with sorcery and the mandrake of fable. The association with Circe, wrong from the start, was perpetuated in many languages—Anglo-Saxon Elfthone, German Hexenkraut, French Enchanteresse, English Witch flower. Dioscorides, or whoever was the father of medical botany, must have had to invent names for unfamiliar plants, by what coincidence or freakish association of ideas we shall never know; and later attempts at identification of the Mediterranean herbs of the early Greek writers with British plants caused more confusion than unquestioning copyings through the ages. By the seventeenth century it had been decided by French botanists (*lutetiana* means 'Parisian') that *Circaea lutetiana* was our enchanter's nightshade, but still the 'why' of the choice is unexplained: its dark woodland habitat is shared by much witchier plants, while the superstition that the tiny perforations in its leaves were the work of the Devil sounds as if the barrel had been scraped for evidence.

'Garden weed' it may be, spreading rapidly and wide as ground cover, but 'unattractive' it emphatically is not, and 'Wild London Pride' is its most apt as well as its prettiest name. Its branching inflorescence is extremely graceful; the disposition of its pale little flowers in a spot pattern over the dark background of the wood is very charming, and the flowers themselves were they larger would be seen to share the colours of the horse chestnut—red in bud, calyx and pistil, pink and white in petals, brownish yellow in the stamens. They are very odd in that they have two of everything—two sepals, two petals, two stamens, a double pistil, and two fruits, which when ripe are hooked like goosegrass. Their stems too have the curious

---

[1] Grattan and Singer: *Anglo-Saxon Magic and Medicine*.

164

Enchanter's Nightshade

unflowerlike habit of slanting downwards. This may more effectually disperse the seeds, but is also designed for pollination, a fly when alighting on the style dragging the stamens under it. Another insect visiting the plant is the leafcutter bee, that takes circular bites from the leaves to line its cells. Devil's work?

WOOD CRANESBILL

Geranium sylvaticum

To come upon a totally unfamiliar flower, prolific in its native haunt, as when I first saw Bloody cranesbill covering a Northumbrian cliff, is a memorable experience. Hardly less so is finding a plant hitherto known only from books: wood cranesbill (sometimes called, appropriately enough, mountain cranesbill) was spread for me all the way down an inland cliff, a roadside wood in Yorkshire. Both plants very much prefer the North.

Geraniums, garden or wild, are a handsome family. All have leaves interesting in shape, scent, colour or texture. The wood cranesbill's are deeply divided, and in their autumn, like Herb Robert, take on brave red, orange and gold. Some geraniums, including wood cranesbill and again Herb Robert, enhance their petals with a metallic iridescent sheen, while those of wood cranesbill are exquisitely engraved on the darker background in greenish white leading to the white centre, so that against the light the lines show as white and in other facets dark. As a family geraniums ring all the changes on red, blue and white. There is a fine crystalline white wood geranium, beloved of gardeners, rather larger than the wild one.

Wood cranesbill is a purplish blue, the more difficult to establish because of the varying colours of other parts of the flower. Sepals, bracts, top of stalk and stigma are all reddish, while the anthers ripen from pinkish cream streaked with wine to grey-blue or even greenish blue with violet filaments that fade to pale pink! Even the form of the petals can spring surprises, for some nearly achieve the heart shape of a wild rose. The stigma too changes form as well as colour, gradually branching into five curling and ever-reddening tips, surrounded by the sharp rosy points of the sepals. The fruit elongates into the characteristic red stork's beak that has given both English and Latin names. The whole plant at this stage, petals long lost, leaves bright as any flower, is in a way even more striking than in its prime of violet-blue.

Wood Cranesbill

FOXGLOVE

Digitalis purpurea

Why *fox*glove? One used to be taught that it should be 'folks' glove', 'folk' being the fairies, but the unmistakable Anglo-Saxon *foxes glofa* gives the lie to that, and to the derivation from the seventeenth-century botanist Fuchs, who first named the plant *Digitalis* from *digitabulum*, 'thimble', an apter word than 'glove'. This prompts the side-track question of how early such refinements were used in sewing: the metal thimble did not appear till the eighteenth century, the earlier protection being of leather, a finger-stall in fact, for preventing instead of covering a wound.

Finger-stall then, and *purpurea*, the original meaning being not purple but crimson; but 'fox'? The story that the wicked fairies helped the fox to shoe himself with foxglove bells so that he might not be heard—or traced?— stealing chickens is unconvincing to say the least. 'Fox' was more likely one of those words which denote an inferior variety; but the choice of fox rather than another animal may have some link with the Reynard stories which date from thirteenth-century France and must have been current, orally and more widely, much earlier. The Norwegian name Revbielde, meaning fox bell, seems to confirm this. And certainly many folk names for the foxglove are connected with magic—Fairy bells, Fairy thimbles, Witches' gloves. These with the group of 'dead' names, such as Dead men's fingers, show that the plant's sinister poisonous properties were long known. Mary Webb's 'Precious Bane' tells of the foxglove-leaf tea that Gideon Sarn prepared for his old mother, and her dying words, 'A bitter brew!'

'Foxgloves are not used in Physicke by any judicious man that I know' says Parkinson pointedly. Present-day medicine could still have been ignorant of the virtues of *digitalis* but for the enterprise of one Dr. Withering. Instead of pooh-poohing the old wives' tales, he noted their successful use of foxglove, especially for dropsy, made a thorough investigation of some two hundred cases, and published the results in 1785. Later the connection with the action of the heart was established, and the subtle balance of the correct dose. Herbalists still consider our wild native plant by far the most reliable and efficacious.

It is not always that anything so invaluable is so spectacular. On a long drive through open country in late June to come suddenly upon a phalanx of six-foot-tall magenta spires, with now and again a white one, bright against dark pines or rising from the bracken of forest clearing or hedgerow, is to enter a new world—no more wild clematis and meadow cranesbill but sweet chestnut and heather, for wild foxglove will thrive only on acid soil.

Nor is there anything sinister at close quarters, when the beautiful grey plush of stem and underleaf is revealed, and the point of the homelier names—Lady's slipper, Snapdragon and Beehive, becomes apparent, for the topmost buds, before upper and lower lip part, are the shape of a Dutch sabot. The open bells, deeper and deeper red as they descend, are full of humblebees attracted by the scattered spots of richer crimson, each set in a circle of white, and crowding closer towards the throat. Still lower, the bells have fallen, playthings to sheathe the fingers of children, leaving the fruit protruding its stigma like a forked tongue and the calyx faintly dyed as if by the red of the lost flower.

Foxglove

SPIKED STAR OF BETHLEHEM

Ornithogalum pyrenaicum

Since the common name for this plant, indeed the only name in the Clapham/Tutin/Warburg Flora, is Bath asparagus, sometimes corrupted to 'sparrow-grass', the secret of its chief location is out: Gerard and contemporaries of his name the exact woods. In 1975 it was still occasionally sold as asparagus in Bath, though the increasing sensitivity to conservation may discourage the outrage—outrage because the flower is extremely beautiful, and because outside the limited area where it was 'almost as abundant as grass' in 1650, and still flourishes, it is not plentiful even in the few southern counties where it grows, strikingly tall and pale against the dark background of leaf and branch and undergrowth.

In early June, when the buds form a spiral like young wheat, it is easily mistaken for asparagus, which happens to be also of the Liliaceae family. By the end of the month the long stout spike of some fifty flowers is quite four feet high, the topmost still asparagus-like, the lowest already forming fat rounded fruit, and the middle bearing delicate six-pointed stars, the deeply grooved petals a greenish cream backed with green, the stamens, broadening at the base, so set as to make a central star of pale gold double spots. The long thin reed-like leaves soon fade and wither at the tips, the plant relying thenceforth for nourishment on its bulb.

Parkinson must mean the little low-growing milkwhite Star of Bethlehem, *Ornithogalum umbellatum,* when he says it was 'much eaten by poore people in Italy, either rawe or roasted, being sweeter in taste than any Chesnut, and serving as well for a necessary food as for delight'. Other European peoples took it in dried form as iron rations on their journey to Mecca. Perhaps therefore the strange names 'dove's dung' and *ornithogalum* ('bird's milk') may refer to the flecks of white stars, or maybe the white bulbs dug up for collection, all over the fields where it grew. Other species of *ornithogalum,* some poisonous, have been used in medicine, but neither our tall woodland Spiked Star nor *Ornithogalum umbellatum,* probably a garden escape in this country, had any other use than as food. The Little Star

172

Spiked Star of Bethlehem

of Bethlehem is hardy, and must have spread by seed as well as by bulb throughout Mediterranean country in spite of these age-long depredations; hence the names *pyrenaicum,* Spanish Star and Star of Hungary. Its constellations still light the way around Provençal cherry orchards in spring.

Seed Heads of Spiked Star of Bethlehem

PIGNUT

Conopodium majus

Pignut is one of the less well-known umbels. Everybody recognises 'Queen Anne's lace', applying the pretty name not only to cow parsley but to all the parsleys, the dropworts and their hedgerow kin. But pignut is a smaller, slighter plant, coming later in the year and growing not by roadsides but in woods, and far more sparely than the crowded bridle ways wear their Queen Anne's lace.

More sparely—but was it always so? Gerard writes 'There is a field adjoining to Highgate, on the right side of the middle of the village, covered over with the same, and likewise in the next field to the conduit heads by Maribone, near the way that leads to Padington by London.' 'Covered over' would hardly describe its growth anywhere today. Has its usefulness been its downfall?

Many people who have never seen pignut to recognise it will know of it through Caliban's words: 'I with my long nails will dig thee pignuts'. Shakespeare must have done it as a boy, though long indeed would the nails have to be that could dig deep enough, following the single stem down to unearth the curious knobbly brown tuber—anything but 'cone-footed', which is the translation of *conopodium*. Is the game worth the candle? Hardly, even to a boy, though the 'nut', white within, is crisp and tasty, something between sweet chestnut, unripe hazelnut and celeriac. Gerard tells us that the Dutch 'doe use to eat them boiled and buttered, as we do Parseneps and Carrots, which so eaten comfort the stomacke'. Is 'pig' merely derogatory? Were pigs trained to find the delicacies as they did truffles in the Dordogne? More likely, as mediaeval manorial deeds suing for trespass suggest, when every cottage had its pig their owners contrived to let them stray into the woods, to feed on more than acorns and beechmast, and what is uprooted does not grow again.

That is a pity, for pignut is a very charming plant. It is the most fragile of the woodland umbels. Even the whiteness of its flowers is subdued with a hint of green. The umbel is arranged with the mathematical precision of its

176

Wood Sage, Wood Avens and Pignut

order to give each head fullest advantage—which gives maximum delight to the eye, proof if one were needed of fitness for purpose. Enjoying this, one is aware of two kinds of flowers, each plant having one kind only. In the male the five little petals are more obvious; in the female the two stigmas, curling away from each other, are more prominent. The leaves, needle-thin in the upper reaches of the stem, are as dainty as the flowers, and make an all-over pattern like a Morris Willow paper against the dark of the wood.

WOOD SAGE

Teucrium scorodonia

Before it is fully open in July wood sage, low-growing, in colour the inconspicuous pale yellow-green of its thinly grassed ground, could be easily dismissed as some kind of heath or bartsia still in bud. Perhaps it is never seen here quite as spectacularly as flanking a quiet road that winds and climbs between woods on its way through bracken and sweet chestnut to the Alps, enjoying every condition it likes—sparse shade, sandy but well drained soil, and no disturbance; but it is not uncommon in Britain, and I have found a wood full of it. It is then that it makes its impact not only *en masse* but as an individual.

The structure of the plant is extremely beautiful—an erect crocketed spire, packed down one side with buds like diminutive ears of corn, a shorter row branching out on either side below. The buds open into a slender hooded flower whose pale catkin-coloured petals complement the purple dye of the stamen filaments and of the stem.

It is immediately recognisable as a sage, a labiate with a fine network pattern deeply engraved into its leaves. They lack however the characteristic and not altogether pleasant sage smell, having rather a whiff of hops, and when crushed of garlic (*scorodonia*), which explains its early name of garlic

178

sage. Neither this flavour nor its bitter taste of gallic acid would seem to recommend it for 'tunning' (clearing and flavouring) ale, yet it shared that with ground ivy among its many uses.

However, in the floras it is to be found not with the sages but with the germanders, and one name for it is germander sage. 'Germander' is supposedly a corruption of a Low Latin word, itself a garble of two Greek words meaning 'on the ground' and 'oak', the latter no more appropriate to wood sage than to germander speedwell. *Teucrium* is named after some Teucer who used the plant in medicine, and could be either Dr. Teucer, a medical botanist, or Teucer King of Troy. The earliest use of sage certainly goes far back into the seeds of time, that is of magic. Translated from the Latin one recipe runs: 'Take a leaf of sage and place it beneath the tongue of a sick man who cannot speak well, and immediately he will speak if he is not doomed to die, but if he is doomed to die he will not speak.'

'A man cannot die if he has sage in his garden' runs the old country saying. It is the true garden sage that one imagines, but Parkinson says 'the small sage is accounted to be of the more force and vertue'. Does he mean wood sage? Very likely before the cottager had a cottage garden he used it as a salve and for inward 'burstings' as well, and as garden sage still is today, for the 'rotelynge in the throte' and 'the perliouse coughe'.

WOOD AVENS

Geum urbanum

The first encounter with wood avens for those keener on country walks than on botany may well be in late summer, when they try to free themselves from the balls of crimson hooks that cling to socks and jeans as they brush through a wood. These are the 'achenes', the surviving styles adapted to carrying out their task of seed dispersal. Poised ready for escape on their thin straggling stems, the fruits become more interesting than were the rather sparsely set flowers. But these have the beauty of all the Rosaceae family, which has enshrined the five-pointed star in heraldry, in embroidery, in carvings of wood and stone: five golden petals with another thinner star of green sepals filling the spaces between the gold; at the back a third star of smaller sepals, and at the front the cluster of future seeds sprinkled round with yellow stamens—it all cries out for celebration in art.

Another common name for wood avens is Herb Bennet, *benedictus* or 'blessed', because it was supposed to keep away evil spirits, by the clove-like perfume of its roots according to folklore, and according to the mediaeval Church by the symbolism of the five wounds of Christ. *Geum* may come from the Greek word for 'scent'; the use of *urbanum* is obscure. 'Avens' is derived from the mediaeval Latin *Avencia*, of unknown origin. Could it be a form of Avicenna (Chaucer's Avycen), the prince of doctors, born in 980 A.D.? The use of its roots in both medicine and magic must date back to that time: it should be dug on the twenty-fifth of March (Lady Day); it would keep away 'venomous beasts'—and moths; it would cure fever, soothe and stimulate. It gave flavour to ale, and boiled in wine made a cordial against the plague—one of the few medicines, one imagines, that were palatable.

WATER AVENS

Geum rivale

Never shall I forget my first sight of water avens. I had come an interminable jouney from London to be interviewed for my first post, and that evening was taken for a cuckoo-haunted walk among primroses and bluebells and fresh young beech leaves by the river Aln. Suddenly, bordering the water, there was a long stretch of these lovely, astonishing flowers. Forgetting where I was and why, I rushed to them with a cry of ecstasy. This place was Paradise. And if ever later on there came times when it was not altogether so, I had only to recall that May evening to know how fortunate I was.

When, many years later, I found water avens along the roadside ditch and in the woodland rides less than an hour's walk from my own home four hundred miles further south, I scarcely recognised it. Here were the drooping columbine-like heads, the flagrant combination of dull purple and orange, but how much smaller and lower-growing! And now that I could walk among them and look closely, what variety! Though many were dwarfish others were nearly as fine as those northern ones. Some faces inside their dark bonnets were palest yellow, some salmon pink; some heads turned up, some down; some were bell-shaped, some opening out; and many were double. It was not surprising to read that they intermarry easily with wood avens, making what the botanist calls 'hybrid swarms', *Geum intermedium*. Strange, this rich and royal juxtaposition of wine and apricot— wine sepals, apricot petals; though Nature has cruder versions, for instance in the bright violet and orange of Alpine toadflax.

Among the more interesting names of water avens, the commonest of which are understandably of the 'button' and 'granny bonnet' sort, is 'Egyptian' or 'gypsy', suggesting both the alien darkness of the hooding sepals and the daring contrast. Another is the Canadian version, 'Indian chocolate'. 'Cure-all' shows that it was assumed to share the magical healing properties of the kindred wood avens. The kinship is more obvious when the pistils, which ripen later than the stamens, lengthen into the reddish curved hooks that will carry the seeds to everything they touch.

M*

Water Avens

YELLOW BIRD'S-NEST
Monotropa hypopithys

As this plant is continually confused with bird's-nest orchid the distinction had better be established straight away. They have little in common except 'tangling roots platted or crossed one over another very intricately, which resembleth a crow's nest made of sticks' (Gerard), though less like a bird's nest than the incurving head of wild carrot which country people call by that name. Nor is yellow bird's-nest an orchid at all: it has some kinship with wintergreen (*Pyrola*). However, both it and bird's-nest orchid—tall, hard and brown—are saprophytes, leafless and devoid of all green colour, deriving their food from dead matter.

They are likely therefore to be found in similar places, beneath trees, on a thick carpet of decaying leaves. *Hypopithys* could mean 'below pine', where little else will grow, though yellow bird's-nest sometimes chooses birch, willow, or more often beech, which is preferred by bird's-nest orchid.

Though widespread, yellow bird's-nest is not common, but is unmistakable when one does find it. It has a soft yet scaly stalk of pale semi-translucent brownish yellow, pushing up from its bed of rich humus and hanging its small head of wax-coloured bell-shaped flowers. Such a strange thing might be expected to smell rank or at best mushroom-like, but it has a sweet almost primrosy scent attractive to insects. As the fruit ripens the stem straightens and the seeds, so fine that Gerard calls them 'unprofitable or barren dust and no seed at all', are scattered by the wind. New plants arise less from this unprofitable dust than from buds formed in the root system.

For Gerard the plant was so rare that he spreads himself on the finding of it, only once, and in Kent. Goodyer, friend of Gerard's editor Johnson, goes into even more detail on the specimen he found on August 22nd, 1620, in a hedgerow near a footpath leading to Waltham. It must have been already in fruit, for he calls it 'round, as big as a pease, so that it resembleth ye suckbottle which children use to suck their drinke out of, having small chives growing round about it with purplish tops'.

183

Yellow Bird's-nest

NETTLE-LEAVED BELLFLOWER
Campanula trachelium

Nettle-leaved bellflower is neither a common nor a prolific plant even in Southern England, and is not found in the North, which however the Giant bellflower, *Campanula latifolia,* prefers. Yet in the limestone woods it chooses it can hardly escape notice, not only because it grows to three or four feet, in stately command of the borders and pathways, but because its fine purple bells, hanging by ones and twos, may be the only flowers to be seen in late July and August. The creamy foam of 'Farewell summer' (meadowsweet) has faded from the ditches, and open glades are snowing rosebay seed. No wonder 'Harvest bells' is among the occasional names of this campanula.

Gerard noted that it grew in several places in Kent, Canterbury included, but called it Coventry bells. Canterbury bells in the Middle Ages meant the annual trip to the shrine of Thomas à Becket, which became something of a jamboree:

'Everie towne that they come through, what with the noice of their singing, and with the sound of their piping, and with the jangling of their Canterburie bels, and with the barking out of dogges after them, they make more noice than if the king came there away with all his clarions and many other minstrels.'[1]

We remember the Miller bagpiping Chaucer's pilgrims out of town, the Sumnour's 'stiff burdoun' to the Pardoner's song 'Come hider love to me', and the 'outriding' Monk:

> And whan he rood men mighte his bridel here
> Gynglen in a whistling wind as clere
> And eek as loude as dooth the chapel belle
> Ther as this lord was keper of the celle.

The Canterbury bell of our gardens is squat and clumsy compared with these gracefully shaped, sharply cut flowers, creased into neat folds in bud

[1] William Thorpe, a Lollard, quoted by Anne Pratt.

and curving open to show a small yellow cross at the base of the elegant violet throat—the stigma, covered in pollen. The doctrine of signatures suggested that here was a cure for infections of the throat and tonsils. The names *Trachelium,* Throtewort and Halswyrt (Anglo–Saxon *heals* means 'neck') show the long use of the concoctions made from its nettle-like leaves.

Nettle-leaved Bellflower

DEADLY NIGHTSHADE

Atropa belladonna

Deadly nightshade looks poisonous. The handsome plum-coloured flower, shaped like a Canterbury bell though half its size, becomes a great polished black cherry held in a five-sepalled cup, alluring to a thirsty traveller as the fruit in 'Goblin Market' and as fatally sweet and juicy. Anne Pratt recounts with relish the calamities it has caused, especially with children, who probably ate it in quantity.

If you 'know of a site' you may find it there year after year, for it spreads by underground rhizome which anchors the tall tough stem to the abandoned chalk quarry or sloping rocky limestone it has chosen as its woodland home. But its habitat is often as sinister as its name—the crumbling ruins of abbeys or castles where it was deliberately grown for its many uses in medicine. A valley near Furness Abbey was known by its folk-name of Bishopswort.

In those days the treatment was frighteningly hit or miss, especially as its poisonous yet magical property, atropine, varies considerably in potency from plant to plant. It is found chiefly in leaves and root, and surprisingly least of all in berry. If the hand has any abrasion one is advised not even to touch the plant. The Scots are said to have subdued the invading Danes by intoxicating them with belladonna juice mixed into their food. This could throw light on the earlier name for the plant, 'dwale', glossed as 'sleep', of Scandinavian origin—although both plant and word occur mainly in the southern counties, where Scandinavian influence on the language was rare. Certainly 'dwale' was used, with other herbs, as a primitive anaesthetic 'for to make a man slepe while men kerven him', and the sense seems to be connected with the earlier meaning of 'dwell', 'to stay put'.

Atropine (the word derived from Atropos, the third of the three Fates, who cut the thread of life) was isolated by the chemist Brandes. 'The Botanic Garden' of 1825 reported that 'the malignant vapour generated during the process obliged him to relinquish his experiments on it', and it was not until 1860 that it was used scientifically and safely in medicine, both

Deadly Nightshade

internally and externally. In eye clinics it is indispensable for dilating the pupil, a cosmetic power exploited through the ages by the *bella donna* who has now taken to eye shadow.

Before the 1914–18 war deadly nightshade was imported mainly from Hungary, and when that supply suddenly ceased our own countryside was raided for it. It is now grown commercially, especially in Russia. Its rarity as a wild flower is probably due also to deliberate extermination as 'dangerous', and no doubt other Solanaceae, all poisonous in some degree—henbane, thorn apple, woody nightshade—share its fate. To read the Ministry of Agriculture's pamphlet on poisonous plants (1954) is to marvel that a single wild flower has anywhere been spared. And since its publication, what more devilish poisons have not been deliberately and permanently launched on the whole earth?

MARTAGON LILY

Lilium martagon

What woodland country was this when martagon lilies grew everywhere wild, as they grow still in a certain gloomy wood, perhaps the only one, in the Cotswolds! These exotic-looking flowers, such tall lily-wands as choirs of Botticelli angels might poise in warm Italian skies, are strange visitants among sturdy English hazels and larches. Nor even in this one spot are they always easy to find, for at first their whorls of leaves scarcely show above the thick dark foliage around, and by the time they flower, in late June, slugs have made merciless inroads upon them, and what might have been a flourishing colony has been reduced here to a sickly circle of leaves, there to a broken column. And then at last you find perfect plants, tier upon tier of leaves rising up stately stems more than four feet high.

The unopened flower is greenish cream, as though it would blossom out into white, though the very end of the drooping bud is tipped with deep wine. As June becomes July the petals open and curve outwards. Daily they curl back a little more till they have taken on their full shape, the cusped crown of some Oriental monarch, or to mediaeval fancy the Turk's cap or 'martagon' that gives the lily its name, with the rust-coloured stamens stiffly protruding; and daily they flush deeper till they are a dull rose like the potter's pink of tempera painting, flecked with Indian red.

Virgil names it among the flowers beloved by bees; Gerard grew it for its beauty alone: 'The flowers be . . . of an overworne purple, spotted on the inside with many smal specks of the colour of rusty iron. The whole floure doth turne itselfe backward at such time as the sun hath cast his beames upon it, from the middle whereof do come forth tender pendants hanging thereat, of the colour the floure is spotted with . . . There hath not bin anything left in writing either of the nature or vertues of these plants: notwithstanding we may deem, that God which gave them such seemly and beautifull shape hath not left them without their peculiar vertues, the finding out whereof we leave to the learned and industrious searcher of Nature.'

Martagon Lily

GLADDON

Iris foetidissima

At first sight the wood seems very unpropitious. It is a small oak wood, old and neglected, surrounded by rusty barbed wire save where a hasty breach has been made by an itinerant tree-feller taking advantage of the Dutch elm disease scare. Severed boughs he dared not stop to collect lie in the wake of the abducted oak trunk, amid a tangle of nettles, brambles, dog's mercury, and apparently nothing else. It is early August, not a time when woodland is at its best.

But what are those ghostly spires? They are the Spiked Star of Bethlehem, now over and forming fruit. A likely place for meadow saffron, neither in leaf nor in flower at present. And then—the unmistakable bright green clumps of sword-shaped leaves like river flags, some of the swords rippled at the edges. From the centre of each rises a gladdon iris, sheathed with leaves on either side of the hidden stem stiff as gladiolus—the word derived from the same root meaning 'sword'. Some flowers are already over, their triangular ovaries rapidly swelling with the fruit that will turn to three rows of bright orange-scarlet beads, bursting their papery walls. Some plants are barren, but others are still in bloom, never more than four flowers to a plant. The form is the magically heraldic fleur-de-lys—three groups of three, set alternately, all coloured and so all looking like petals. The three largest and most spectacular are properly sepals, a subtle blue-grey edged with dull purple, exquisitely pencilled in darker purple, while the innermost three, erect and merging into honey-guiding yellow at the base, surprisingly have the function of both stamen and stigma.

A strange plant indeed, with some strange names. Roast beef iris, like *foetidissima*, refers not very appropriately to its odour when crushed, and the various country nicknames with 'dragon' or 'snake' may allude to this, or to the inviting berries perhaps confused with those of wild arum or spurge laurel. If so these names too are misleading: this plant is not poisonous, and its roots have been used as a purge (with ale and castor oil seeds, which might help!) down the centuries. Mrs. Grieve's 'modern' herbal still calls it 'taken

N

193

inwardly and applied outwardly an excellent remedy for scrofula'.

Even when all the seeds have disappeared we can still find gladdon by its leaves, which stay green through all winters except the hardest. Nor will it be only in woods, though it likes shelter. It also likes moisture, but with good drainage, especially on the chalky soils it seems to prefer, and therefore on sloping terrain such as on Wansdyke beneath shrubs, and even to leeward of sand dunes stabilised by marram grass, among which its strong rhizomes can find anchorage.

Gladdon

VIOLET HELLEBORINE
Epipactis sessilifolia

We had to be taken to the wood, a very ordinary abandoned coppice in rather dull flat country, where this exciting plant had been discovered by a forester on his rounds not looking either for it or for anything violet. Nor did he tell us what to expect: we merely followed through the pathless jungle of undergrowth that caught our feet as we stumbled after him. The overcrowded saplings had grown so high that the place was gloomy, the more so for a glory beyond the distant fringe of the wood where the sun caught a border of hogweed in full bloom.

All at once we were arrested—there is no other word for it—by a single plant, search-lighted by a penetrating ray of sun: a spiralling cascade of pale five-pointed stars that took our breath away. Then, a little further, another; a third; and then six or seven.

Violet the flowers were not—only more violet than those of the duller broad-leaved helleborine that may be found near by. Most were a watery whitish green, enlivened by a delicate pink flush at the tip. Some however were suffused with a cadaverous greyed purple, their pale green stalks tinged with mauve, and here and there the undersides of the dark leaves could be said to be violet indeed. Neither of course had the flowers five simple petals: they were shaped like those of any other orchid, yet so disposed around their tall spires in a constellation of forty to fifty that 'starry helleborine' would be the most appropriate clue for a seeker.

Where the flowers were spent they hung down the long stem as stiff and swollen seed capsules, polished, corrugated and brown. Now in August the one luminous enchantment of the wood, by autumn the plants would stand as dark skeletons hardly visible against the fallen leaves.

Violet Helleborine

BROAD-LEAVED HELLEBORINE

Epipactis helleborine

Since every plant is unique each gives a peculiar pleasure. Broad-leaved helleborine's is its greeting in a 'dankish and shadowie' beechwood in mid-August, or even in September, when all is expected to be closed down for the winter. At first the ground cover seems to be nothing but curled beech leaves and detritus. Then, stooping to free our feet from sprawling thorns, we find that they have also caught sanicle seeds, and that wild strawberry and woodruff have grown here and there.

A little further into the wood and, as we had hoped, we come upon the tall stately stalks of the *Epipactis,* laden with fruit below but still in flower for a third or more of their twenty to forty inches. We cannot resist counting—twenty-four flowers a good average, let alone the fruiting, and forty-six on the biggest. They are said to have scored a hundred.

Individually however the flowers are not spectacular. They droop slightly; they have no long spur like the butterfly orchid, being pollinated by the short-tongued wasp; and their colour is at first sight dingy. Only at first sight though: were they larger those dusky pink lower lips would be thought beautiful, especially complemented by the subdued yellowish-green of other parts of the flower, though they vary greatly, pale or dark. And those long ribbed fruits, rapidly swelling and darkening, with a tassel of dead petals at the end—if all their seeds scatter what need of the stout underground stem, already forming next year's buds? But Nature takes no chances.

'Broad-leaved', a comparative term, applies only to the leaves in the middle of the stem, so deeply veined as to look almost fluted. Say two inches wide to five long, they are broader than the ground leaves of *Epipactis sessilifolia,* violet helleborine. *Epipactis* was thus named by Dioscorides, and though every syllable now lightly repeated by mankind once had significance, what he meant by it is now lost. And why helleborine? The stiff leaf-clasped stem of broad-leaved helleborine bears a slight resemblance to a *veratrum,* not wild in this country, wrongly called white hellebore. One might prefer ignorance to such an 'explanation'.

198

Broad–leaved Helleborine

ROSEBAY WILLOW-HERB
Chamaenerion angustifolium

The strangest thing about rosebay willow-herb is the way that in the last century it has become one of our commonest weeds, persecuted in gardens, where it spreads by root as well as by windborne seed; and its acres of crude unvaried pink can sound a harsh note among the harmonising olives, browns and greys of the countryside. In Gerard's time it was rare enough for him to note, as was his wont, the exact provenance and habitat of the specimen sent to him. J. Smith (Sowerby, 1820) tells us that 'Mr. Winch observed it on the Cheviot hills', and Anne Pratt (1855) describes it as 'a rare plant in moist woods in England, though less so in Scotland'. Yet its many names testify to its having been familiar enough in the interval. What ensured its survival was gardens, where it grew 'very goodly to behold . . . garnished with brave flowers of great beauty' (Gerard). Garden soil must have been much disturbed, and also frequently scattered with wood ash, so maybe the plant, having developed a strong adaptability to these two conditions, was the quicker to spread when roads and railways began to be built everywhere, with consequent destruction and burning of woodland, and again later when 'enemy action' provided fresh sites. Hence the American name fireweed. The biggest concentration I have ever seen—in the odd company of equally prolific mare's tail—was from the little train plying between York and Harrogate, that runs right through it.

Its German name is Weidenröschen, 'meadow rose', but though it does prefer the open glade it is intrinsically a woodland plant, and a handsome one, even in its infancy, when the colony of red-tipped young leaves, golden-green at the base, looks like a bed of small rosy gentians. By the time it is five or six feet tall the spindle-shaped spike of pink-stalked flowers is in bloom below, tapering from large to smaller, smallest buds. The petals have an interesting oddity, two being very slightly bigger than the other two, though the narrow crimson sepals showing between fill up the circle prettily. Their colour, diluted with pale stamens and abundant leaves, though hardly Gerard's poetic 'orient purple', is not unpleasant in the single

200

Rosebay Willow-herb

plant. As the fruits lengthen the force of the earlier name *epilobium*, 'upon a pod', becomes apparent. When they burst and scatter their clouds of fluff-encased seeds the massed plants seem at a distance to be smoking. By now the wood looks its untidiest.

One can hardly believe that 'the down of the seeds, mixed with cotton or fur, has been manufactured into stockings' (T. Green's *Universal Herbal*, 1816), but neither are other uses of the plant very convincing. Its young shoots (you have guessed it) have been eaten as asparagus; it has been made into tea and ale, with the additional intoxication of fly agaric, the poisonous scarlet white-spotted toadstool! However, it does contain tannin, which yields tonic properties like those of willow. Hence perhaps the many willow names—Blooming Sally (sallow), Wickup (withy?), French willow, Persian willow; for the leaves, though willow-like, are not more so than those of many another plant. The botanical name *Chamaenerion* means 'ground oleander' and *angustifolium* 'narrow-leaved', that is, with leaves narrower than those of the true oleander, rosebay willow-herb's aristocratic relative.

Assuredly its greatest benefaction to a world increasingly aware of the calamity of disappearing woodland is its contribution to the soil of mycorrhizal fungus used by the roots of trees. Thus it not only clothes bare patches, including slagheaps, but makes reafforestation possible.

MEADOW SAFFRON

Colchicum autumnale

To many of us this plant will conjure up the memory of an autumnal sub-Alpine pasture, its lush grass dotted all over with the pale lilac-pink flowers, six-pointed stars in sunshine or elongated lotus shapes closed under clouded skies. But here in England where it is native, and grows nearly as abundantly in the patches where it still survives—'in fat and fertill medowes about Bathe', for instance—it also likes woodland at any rate in Wiltshire, preferably a rough sparse thicket whose untidy growths protect and support its delicate cups.

Anything so nascent, so vulnerably leafless and naked, may well choose to bloom in mellow September rather than in April, 'the cruellest month', when its handsome polished rich green leaves make conspicuous bunches, marking the place to return to later in the year to find them vanished but the flowers out. This curious behaviour is less odd when one knows the reason: what we call the stem, shining translucent white fine as porcelain, is really an unusually long flower throat, whose ovary at the base is actually underground, where the seeds slowly ripen like those of other plants. But it multiplies also by deeply rooted corms, nourished by those rich green leaves of Spring, which is probably what has saved it from extinction by persecution for its poisonous qualities.

More often than not, meadow saffron is called autumn crocus. Autumnal it is, but crocus it is not, though masquerading as one, and it has to be distinguished because there is a true autumn crocus which also flowers in autumn and puts out its leaves in spring. Botanically this crocus is not of the lily but of the iris family, with violet-blue petals and three gold stamens instead of six; its leaves are the thin dark grasslike leaves of spring crocuses, and it is not a native but an escape.

Meadow saffron then is not autumn crocus; is sometimes 'meadow' but is not the saffron (*sativus*) of Southern Europe, including the neighbourhood of Colchis which has given the name *Colchicum*. It is the dried redgold pistils of this commercially grown plant which are still sold in the markets of

Meadow Saffron

Israel, and in the sparing quantity needed to colour and flavour Easter cake it does no 'churlish working'. It is to be hoped that an equally cautious dose 'pierceth to the heart, provoking laughter and merriment.'[1]

If Meadow saffron is entitled to few of its common appellations it wears its local English names delightfully—Naked ladies, Naked boys, Naked Nanny (Ann), pristine in the tousle of woodland undergrowth, newborn in the fall of the year.

[1] Christopher Cotton, quoted by Edith Wheelwright in *The Physick Garden*.

Epilogue

The forty years of spare time are up and the book completed, no doubt bearing signs of its inevitably overlong gestation. This however has actually helped in one way: it gives a perspective not possible over a short span. When we first began (if there ever was a 'first') to draw and record we went everywhere on foot, thus enjoying many a chance discovery by the way. We tended to take the abundance, the variety and the permanence of Nature for granted: it was a major tragedy if a white lane was tarred. That was before the mighty mechanical saw and excavator, before the obsessive use of herbicides and pesticides, before 'Development'.

Yet it is modern technology that can transport us to still undamaged country with its wild life and flora on the other side of the world, and even relay them to our own firesides, awakening not only love of beauty but thought and conscience. We exploit the natural world at our peril: the woodland of this country could perish like the raped rain-forest of Brazil if man-made desert brought about a global change of climate. Ecology and conservation, comparatively new ideas, are a great hope, perhaps the only hope for the earth we share with animal and plant. Is this due in part to the conquest of space? Undertaken greedily as a competition in national prestige, it brought one unexpected blessing: we saw ourselves in a new dimension. In the words of the Russian cosmonaut:

'Our blue planet looks very beautiful from space, and there is a profound sense of how small, homely and fragile it is. If one is faced plainly with responsibility for its destiny it is quite clear that mankind must do its utmost to see that it remains as it is, both for us and for our descendants—and that it gets better.'

Index

The Cheese Room (1977)